# Health Care Policy Simplified; Understanding A Complex Issue

# Health Care Policy Simplified; Understanding A Complex Issue

A COLLECTION OF ESSAYS
ON HOW TO ACHIEVE ACCESS
TO AFFORDABLE HIGH-QUALITY
HEALTH CARE FOR ALL AMERICANS

Roger A. Stark, MD, FACS

Copyright © 2020 by Roger A. Stark

ISBN: 978-1-59849-283-5

Library of Congress Control Number: 2020903766

Printed in the United States of America

Editor: Danielle Harvey

**www.washingtonpolicy.org**

All rights reserved. No part of this book may be transmitted
in any form or by any means, electronic or mechanical, including
photocopying, recording, or by any information storage or retrieval
system, in part, in any form, without the permission of the author.

Requests for such permissions should be addressed to:

Classic Day Publishing
943 NE Boat Street
Seattle, Washington 98105
206-860-4900
www.classicdaypub.com

# Endorsements

"In a very readable and easily understood book, Dr. Stark presents a strong case for less government and more patient control in our health care system. He provides the history that brought the country to this point of ever-rising health care costs. He discusses the various parts of our health care system and how they relate to the growing crisis of care.

Ultimately, he provides free-market solutions to this complex system. As in any other economic activity, patients should have the ability to become consumers of health care. Stark believes that patients are the most important part of the health care equation and should have timely access to prices and outcome results. Once armed with this information, they can control their own health care decisions without the interference of government bureaucrats."

*Former Oklahoma U.S. Senator Tom Coburn, MD*

"As reforms of health care delivery systems and health insurance continue to be part of an ongoing national discussion, Dr. Stark gives an important overview of what we currently have and what paths we need to take—from the perspective of someone who has actually delivered medical care. That perspective is usually lacking in health policy discussions—and this book is an important addition for that reason."

*Rep. Andy Harris, MD, Chair of the GOP Doctors Caucus*

"I am always looking for practical solutions to the problems our country faces. Dr. Stark outlines the enormous burden the government has placed on our health care delivery system, and, more importantly, describes solutions that put patients in charge of their own health care decisions—not the government. His book is another example of the excellent work the Washington Policy Center produces."

*Congresswoman Cathy McMorris Rodgers (WA)*

# Table of Contents

This book examines the historical development of health care policy in this county and explains how the system arrived at its present costly, confused, and controversial state.

Together these essays give the reader a fundamental understanding of various parts of the system, and they examine the health care policies in other countries for their relevance to the United States. The book includes proposed reforms which, if adopted, would hold down costs, provide more choices, and put patients—not the government—in charge of important health care decisions.

The book may be read from beginning to end, but central themes are repeated so that readers may start the book at any chapter of interest.

The last chapter provides a collection of opinion articles that have been published in recent years. These will give the reader a sense of the pertinent health care issues and the free-market arguments that have been made in the public debate for more patient control and less government dominance over our health care system.

# Introduction

Health care is one of the most personal activities humans experience and is undeniably a necessity of life. Everyone, from a newborn baby to a senior facing death, has interacted with the health care system in some way.

Medical care delivery, especially in the United States, has become extremely complex. Most people have an impression of health care based on their own interactions with providers, hospitals, clinics, and pharmacies. People see a part of the system but not the entire picture.

Countless papers and books have been written about the U.S. health care system, many of which go into great detail on specific policy areas. This book provides a broad overview of health care and is designed for the general public. It briefly describes the important parts of the system and distills complex issues into easily understandable topics. Some areas are covered in detail, whereas others are meant to provide background and hopefully stimulate further investigation on the part of the reader.

Even though medical care is very personal, the overall industry is enormous. In 2018, the total cost of health care in the U.S. was $3.65 trillion, which represented 17.9 percent of the economy or the gross domestic product (GDP).[1] Compare this to the $27.2 billion, or five percent of the GDP, spent in 1960.

The Centers for Medicare and Medicaid Services (CMS) predicts that health care spending will continue to rise to 20 percent of the country's GDP by 2025.[2] This is not a sustainable growth rate and places health care spending above many other government and life priorities.

---

1    "U.S. Health Care Costs Skyrocketed to $3.65 Trillion in 2018, by E. Sherman, Fortune.com, February 21, 2019, at https://fortune.com/2019/02/21/us-health-care-costs-2/.

2    "CMS: U.S. health care spending to reach nearly 20 percent  of GDP by 2025," Advisory Board, February 17, 2017, at https://www.advisory.com/daily-briefing/2017/02/16/spending-growth.

Health care reform is therefore mandatory. The real question is what direction that reform should take. Should government become more involved, or should patients, as consumers of health care, determine the path to reform?

Whether a person believes that health care is a fundamental right or not, everyone can agree that health care is a necessity of life—just like food, shelter, and clothing. Except, through the use of safety-net programs, the government is not involved and does not provide these other necessities of life. The government does exist to ensure that a free market is available so people have free choices in obtaining these other necessities.

Health care is very personal, but fundamentally it is an economic activity. Free markets in other economic activities have provided Americans with the highest living standards in history. There is no reason to believe that a free market wouldn't work in health care.

The book looks historically at how the country arrived at this point and gives the reader a fundamental understanding of the various parts of the system. It examines the health care systems of other countries and their relevance for the United States. It includes reform measures that will hold down costs, will provide more choices, and will put patients—not the government—in charge of their own health care. Included is a chapter that looks to the future and where our health care delivery system is headed.

The last chapter is a compilation of relevant opinion articles that have been published in the last few years. These will hopefully give the reader a sense of the pertinent health care issues and the free-market arguments for more patient control and less government control of our health care system.

I would like to thank Paul Guppy, Vice President for Research, at Washington Policy Center for his input and assistance with this book.

Roger Stark, MD, FACS
Seattle, Washington
2019

CHAPTER 1

# History

So how did we get into this health care crisis? What historically set us up for the seemingly intractable problems we now face?

Like so many things, we can get a better understanding of our current problems by knowing the crucial steps, and missteps, that the country took along the way. In general, each new law or regulation or program made sense at the time it was enacted, but it was not necessarily made in the context of our overall health care system. There was no master plan or overall design as health care policy was developed in the United States.

Multiple political agendas, pressures from the choices other countries were making, and an accepted philosophy that health care is a "right" to which we are all entitled led to our medical system developing much differently than that of any other service or commodity in the United States.

The history of health care can be divided chronologically in any number of ways. To simplify things and to use several logical milestones, the book looks at three periods; the pre-Depression era, 1930–1965, and the 1960s up to today.[3]

## The period before the Great Depression

To start from the beginning, there were a number of colonial and then state-sponsored programs that provided care for specific groups and communities in the 1600s and 1700s. The first significant federal program was passage of the 1799 Act for Relief of Sick and Disabled Seamen. This program became the U.S. Marine Service and, ultimately, at the turn of the twentieth century, became what we now know as the U.S. Public Health Services (USPHS).

Originally, the USPHS managed quarantine issues and the funding of medical research. In the early 1900s, the agency grew to include school health and vaccinations, and received federal funding to operate multiple health clinics throughout the United States. The next one hundred years saw this organization expand tremendously, with an annual budget approaching $100 billion by the end of the twentieth century. Today, the USPHS is involved in several social issues, such as cigarette smoking, alcohol abuse, family planning, as well as management of the Indian Health Service.

Congress established the National Academy of Sciences in 1863 to study health care issues nationwide. In 1879, the National Board of Health was created specifically to control epidemics. On the local front, aseptic and antiseptic practices were not only becoming common, but were reassuring people that hospitals were safe and really could heal the sick. From 1873 to 1923, the number of hospitals in the U.S. grew from 178 to 6,830, most of which were built by charities and religious organizations.

The American Medical Association (AMA) was formed in the mid-nineteenth century to promote safe medicine and to protect the interests of patients and doctors. From the beginning, however, the AMA was heavily politicized, and its leaders had very definite ideas concerning appropriate medical practice. It opposed physicians contracting with fraternal lodges because of "ruinous competition" and refused membership into county medical societies to those doctors that did contract their services. Likewise, the AMA opposed and fought physicians' participation in prepaid health care, which had become common with large companies in dangerous industries, such as mining and logging.

By the end of the nineteenth century, health care was already divided along national lines and local  private or charity offerings. Most citizens at that time believed the federal government should participate in major health issues such as epidemiology and the study of the spread of disease. For local, routine care—seeing the doctor or going to a hospital—most people believed in using the private system.

Internationally, however, the socialist and labor movements lobbied heavily for nationalized health care during the late nineteenth and early twentieth centuries. Germany, in 1883, became the first country to formally provide comprehensive state-run medicine. In the U.S., the Socialist Party pushed for socialized medicine in the 1904 presidential election, and the Progressive Party of Theodore Roosevelt made socialized medicine a campaign issue in 1912.

At that same time, twelve state legislatures considered bills for compulsory health care, and more than one governor expressed support for the concept.

By World War I, more than ten European countries had socialized their medical care systems. Enthusiasm for socialized health care in the U.S., however, waned tremendously after the war because of its negative association with Germany and Russia. Voters were also smart enough to realize there was no real need to socialize their medical care. No state passed any form of government-run health care, and only sporadic interest existed on a national level. While charities and religious groups built the hospitals, fraternal orders and lodges offered their members a form of health and life insurance. Less than ten percent of the country had any type of personal health insurance during the early twentieth century.

As lines were being drawn over who was providing what type of care, physician training was also coming under considerable scrutiny at the beginning of the twentieth century. In 1910, the Carnegie Foundation commissioned a study to examine physician education in the U.S. The result of this study, the Flexner Report, recommended state licensing of graduates from qualified medical schools only. Prior to this report, medical training was offered at various types of schools with no standardized graduation requirements and no assurance of quality. The number of medical schools in this country subsequently dropped from 131 to 69 in the next 34 years, care became more standardized, and the quality of care improved.

The 1920s saw an extension of veterans' benefits after World War I. Congress established the Veterans Bureau in 1921, and by 1929, several of these programs were consolidated into the Department of Veterans Affairs. On an international scope, Europe was rebuilding after World War I, and the nationalization of health care became commonplace.

Basically, life was good in the U.S. during the 1920s—we had won the Great War, the economy was booming, unemployment was low, and health care was not an issue for most people. Interestingly enough,however, the first comprehensive study of the U.S. health care system was undertaken in 1927. A small group of national leaders, including many physicians, formed the Committee on the Costs of Medical Care (CCMC), which was funded by eight philanthropic foundations. In spite of widespread opposition to socialized medicine in the U.S., the CCMC recommended a long-range plan for instituting national health care. Unfortunately, the committee did not even determine, or attempt to estimate, how many people actually lacked access to health care in this country, nor did it estimate a cost for socializing medicine in the US.

Although the CCMC cannot be faulted for failing to predict the technological explosion in health care in the twentieth century, it was totally irresponsible of the committee not to put some type of price tag on socializing medicine in the U.S. Unfortunately, this became a recurring theme as the twentieth century unfolded, where need, predicted benefit, and ultimate cost were, if not totally ignored, at least not emphasized in government intervention in health care in this country.

### The Great Depression to 1960
When the economy went into a tailspin in 1929, the medical sector was not immune to the crash. The average hospital reimbursement dropped from $200 per patient in 1929 to $60 per patient in 1930.

Patients, providers, and hospitals were caught up in the financial uncertainties of the 1930s. The U.S. saw the institution of prepaid health care as a partial answer to the financial insecurity. In 1929, 1,500 school teachers at Baylor University Hospital in Dallas, Texas, started the first group insurance plan. In 1932, Blue Cross, as we know it today, was started by multiple hospitals in the Sacramento, California, area. These programs provided prepaid health care on a group basis and were called medical, or health care, insurance.

From the onset, these plans were not truly "insurance" in the classic sense. Rather they were prepaid health "maintenance" programs in that they covered everything from routine care, such as annual exams to emergency care and other unplanned and unexpected needs for health care—those health events comparable to car insurance covering accidents and homeowner insurance covering fires. This concept of maintenance rather than insurance has survived and has become the accepted definition of health "insurance" (see Chapter 5). It is a colossal misnomer in health care discussions. By 1940, there were multiple prepaid health plans throughout the country, as well as two large health maintenance organizations, the Kaiser Industry Program and the Group Health Association. All were providing coverage for health maintenance care.

As the 1930s progressed, Blue Cross enlarged as it covered hospital expenses, and Blue Shield emerged and expanded to cover physician reimbursement. From a political standpoint, the AMA strongly opposed health maintenance organizations and prepaid plans other than Blue Cross and Blue Shield. The "Blues" were heavily supported by organized medicine and retained that support throughout the twentieth century.

The 1930s saw a huge expansion of both state and federal intervention into many aspects of the U.S. economy, including the health care delivery system. The Ransdell Act of 1930, for example, greatly enlarged the National Institute of Health. Although President Roosevelt was extremely interested in nationalizing health care as part of his New Deal, he never lobbied strongly for it, using the excuse that it was impossible to go up against the medical societies. In reality, however, a massive voter revolt forced Congress to remove the national health care provision from the Social Security legislation of 1935. The majority of people believed they had satisfactory access to health care and did not want the federal government to control their relationships with doctors and hospitals. On the state level, all but four states had compulsory workers' compensation programs in place. Interestingly, in addition to most Americans being satisfied with their health care in the early 1930s, health care at this time accounted for approximately four percent of the GDP, a reasonable and acceptable sum.

The controversy over national social insurance specifically for retirement, in other words Social Security, was taken as high as the Supreme Court. The Court ruled in 1937, in *Helvering v. Davis*, that the concept of a mandatory socialized insurance program was constitutional. That decision laid legal ground work, but again, there was no widespread enthusiasm for the institution of socialized medical insurance in the U.S. at that time.

By 1940, as the debate over nationalizing health insurance continued, Blue Cross had grown to six million members, and commercial insurance had approximately 3.7 million subscribers. Although Blue Cross and commercial insurance carriers were direct competitors, they had several distinct differences. Blue Cross, by law, did not have to hold reserves, had very significant tax advantages, and had no minimum benefit or premium rates. These are advantages that Blue Cross has maintained in various forms down through the years.

As the 1940s unfolded, the health care insurance industry had become fairly mature. Again, it cannot be stressed enough that health "insurance" is clearly different than other forms of true indemnity insurance. Unlike car and home policies that do not even cover routine maintenance, health policies are designed to cover routine medical care and unplanned occurrences.

Also of significance is the fact that doctors were paid through a usual and customary fee arrangement, whereas hospitals were paid on a "cost plus" basis. This was a very convoluted plan that reimbursed hospitals not for a specific service, but on a percentage of their total costs as well as on a percentage of the number of policyholders of any one company using that hospital. Larger hospitals were reimbursed at a higher percentage rate than smaller hospitals. This led to a disincentive for hospitals to control costs since higher reimbursements followed higher expenditures. This bizarre arrangement continues to a degree today and is simply one more piece of the health care crisis puzzle.

World War II brought about many changes in this country, not the least of which was how the federal government impacts people's lives. The U.S. income tax rate increased from four percent in 1939 to 23 percent in 1944. In 1940, 14.6 million people filed income tax returns, and by 1945, 49.8 million people filed returns, although the population had only increased by six percent. Understandably, there was a war to support, yet, unfortunately, the door had clearly been opened to impose an ever increasing tax-and-spend mentality in Washington, D.C.

The other massively significant legislation during World War II was the institution of wage and price controls. The government limited how much employers could pay workers. The War Labor Board, however, established a policy where fringe benefits of five percent of wages could be offered to employees. About the same time, the IRS ruled that health insurance purchases for employees could be deducted for tax purposes by the employer as a legitimate cost of doing business.

Obviously, health insurance then became a prime fringe benefit to offer workers. This concept of tax-free employer-provided health care is now firmly entrenched in this country. Unfortunately, the tax laws have been slanted to allow businesses to deduct health insurance from pre-tax dollars, but until recently, individual purchasers and users of the insurance could not do so. Of course, workers are not required to declare the fringe benefit or health care as income. The statistics for employer-paid health care are very revealing. In 1945, employers paid approximately ten percent of employee health care. By 1950, that number had jumped to 37 percent, and by 1960, larger companies were paying 100 percent of health benefits for their employees.

Enrollment in the hospital-only insurance plans skyrocketed in the last few years of the war from seven million subscribers in 1942 to 26 million subscribers in 1945. Again, the majority of these people had employer-paid health benefits.

The federal government further entrenched itself in health care when it expanded its veterans' care and established the Veterans Hospital Administration system. By 1945, with 91 hospitals, the Veterans Administration system was the largest single health care delivery system in the U.S.

Americans continued to reject nationalizing health care. A poll in 1946 revealed that only one percent of U.S. citizens favored it— even as the government proposed incremental plans to adopt it, with senior citizens as the first target group. The federal government failed in its efforts from the 1930s until 1950 to establish a plan that would completely nationalize medical care delivery. However, Franklin D. Roosevelt, president from 1932 until his death in 1945, favored such a plan, as did President Truman, who followed him.

In 1946, Congress passed the Hill-Burton Act, requiring hospitals to provide free care for 20 years to people who were unable to pay. The bill provided funding for 500,000 additional hospital beds. Federal money of $4.4 billion was added to the $9.1 billion from state and local taxing agencies to fund the program. The Hill-Burton Act expired in 1978, but it clearly set a precedent for substantial government involvement and funding of health care.

It can't be emphasized enough that the poor in this country, both seniors and those under 65, had access to paid health care through the Hill-Burton Act. Of course, this was a disincentive for many people to buy health insurance because they knew they would be covered by the government-mandated program. And remember, this was prior to Medicare and Medicaid legislation in 1965.

Another event that caused health care coverage to increase dramatically was the 1948 Labor Relations Board decision that said unions could negotiate for health care benefits for their members. Down through the years, this has become a huge negotiating point for the unions. In 1949, 2.7 million union workers were covered by health care benefits, exploding to 12 million workers by 1955.

Also, during the post-World War II years, the National Institute of Health expanded from a budget of $180,000 in 1945 to a budget of $400 million in 1960. The National Science Foundation was also started in 1950, and the Department of Health, Education, and Welfare was established in 1953. During the 1950s, the voters understood government funding for broad-based scientific and research organizations, but they still opposed any form of socialized medicine.

Although many government interventions into health care took place during the mid-twentieth century, four significant landmark acts contributed heavily to our current health care crisis.

First, there is the prepaid insurance model set up during the 1930s. It was very clear from the outset that this was not insurance in the traditional sense but was in fact a maintenance health care program. This seemed advantageous to patients as well as to hospitals and providers at that time, but it set a lasting precedent for what we expect health insurance to be.

Second, the cost-plus concept of hospital reimbursement basically rewarded expanded care, expensive services, and greater utilization, all of which created disincentives to control costs.

Third, the fact that employers could take a business income-tax deduction for the cost of employee health benefits definitely entrenched the concept of third-party payers in the latter half of the twentieth century. This originally seemed like a win-win proposition until costs exploded for employers and employees faced limited access options and higher copays. From an economic standpoint, the concept of someone else paying for health care has predictably led to over-utilization and, consequently, exploding costs.

Lastly, the Hill-Burton Act firmly entwined federal government funding with state government funding to subsidize the construction of both public and private hospitals. As part of the deal, the nation's poor were provided government-sponsored health care in a regulated, organized fashion. Although you might think this solved the problem of providing health care for the uninsured poor, in reality, it was one of the first steps to government-run, socialized medicine.

## 1960 to the present

Although the vast majority of people in the U.S. remained opposed to socialized medicine in the 1950s, President Truman, in office from 1945 until January 1953, made several attempts at socializing health care. However, President Eisenhower, who followed him and remained in office until 1961, opposed the idea, and Congress did not seriously consider any health delivery legislation through the mid-to-late 1950s.

The idea of socialized medicine resurfaced when it became a campaign issue in 1960, with President Kennedy favoring a broad-based hospital insurance program through Social Security and President Nixon favoring an expansion of what was later to become the Kerr-Mills law.

By 1960, the majority of employees had health insurance through their employers, and this insurance also covered their families. Today, half of all Americans receive their health insurance from their employer or their spouse's employer. In addition, veterans were covered by both outpatient medical and hospital care through the VA system, and the Indian Health Services covered the Native American population. It was essentially the poor, the elderly, and the unemployed who were not provided specific health care by a third party. It should be noted, however, that they did have hospital coverage through the Hill-Burton Act, and they had access to health insurance through commercial carriers if they chose to buy it.

From 1952 to 1962, the number of seniors with health insurance actually doubled from 30 percent to 60 percent. Elected officials in

Washington, D.C., were still concerned, however, about the low-income senior group. To assist these poorer seniors, the Kerr-Mills law was added to the Social Security Amendments of 1960. This was a landmark bill in the sense that it was a precursor to the 1965 Medicare Act.

The Kerr-Mills law was fairly ingenious in that it was a "means-tested" program. In other words, it provided health care for financially qualified poor seniors based on income. Also, it was a voluntary program, run by the states (although funded by the federal government), and it was actually more generous than Medicare in that it included such things as eye-glasses, prescription drugs, and dental care.

By 1962, at least 60 percent of seniors had individual health care insurance and low-income seniors were taken care of by the Kerr-Mills law. Employees were covered by their employers. There was also a thriving private health insurance market and virtually everyone in the U.S. had access to this market. Charities and county hospital facilities provided care for the poor and indigent through the Hill-Burton Act.

Whether it was simply government bureaucracy or an organized effort to sabotage the Kerr-Mills law, the Health, Education, and Welfare Department (HEW) continually stalled reimbursing states for health care utilization through the program. The suspicion at the time was that HEW officials opposed both the voluntary nature of the program and its means-testing requirement, two features that ran counter to the universal coverage, socialized medicine philosophy.

With President Kennedy's death in 1963, several important things changed in Washington, D.C. First, obviously, Lyndon Johnson, already one of the most powerful political leaders of the time, became president. Second, the Democrats enjoyed a landslide victory in 1964. Third, Johnson's first 100 days in office were more than a honeymoon period with Congress. There was a considerable amount of guilt over President Kennedy's death, and, consequently, it seemed that President Johnson and the Democratic Congress were able to pass much of the legislation that Kennedy had supported.

Health care for seniors was one of Kennedy's main interests, and in 1965, Johnson pushed the Medicare bill through Congress. Interestingly enough, the Medicare bill was tied to a seven percent increase in Social Security benefits for seniors, the first increase since 1959. Obviously, seniors would be much more likely to support any health care legislation that was combined with an increase in their Social Security reimbursement.

The Republicans at the time favored a program called Better Care, which was a voluntary insurance program funded by deducting $3 a month from Social Security and matched by federal funds. Better Care ultimately became Medicare Part B, covering physician reimbursement.

The AMA favored a program called Elder Care, which was essentially an expanded Kerr-Mills program. Elder Care subsequently became Medicaid, providing federal and state funding for the poor and the disabled.

The driving force behind the inclusion of all three programs was Representative Wilbur Mills (D-Ark.), who was Chairman of the House Ways and Means Committee and somewhat of a political genius. At the end of the day, he appeared to give everyone involved what they wanted, and, hence, we wound up with Medicare Parts A and B and Medicaid. The passage of Medicare and Medicaid in 1965 created the largest socialized health care program in the world.

Early Medicare looked great. Seniors were provided with essentially free care, hospitals and doctors were given financial support, and the insurance companies were given the financial benefit of administering the whole program. Not surprisingly, the insurance companies found they could not compete with the government and discontinued private individual policies for seniors. Consequently, the free market for senior health insurance collapsed.

When comparing Medicare with the Kerr-Mills law, several glaring differences stand out. First of all, the Kerr-Mills program was voluntary, whereas Medicare was tied with Social Security benefits. If seniors opted out of Medicare, they would then lose their Social Security benefits; this was not true of Kerr-Mills coverage. Second, there was no means testing for Medicare; it included all seniors regardless of their financial status. And finally, Medicare was less comprehensive than the Kerr-Mills law. Originally, drug benefits, eye-glasses, and dental care were not provided with Medicare like they were under the Kerr-Mills law.

At the time Medicare was instituted in 1965, health care made up 5.9 percent of our gross domestic product. Compare this with health care's 17.9 percent share in 2018.

Although the majority of people in the United States favored some type of assistance for seniors, especially low-income elderly, the specifics of the Medicare bill were a mystery to 75 percent of Americans when it became law.

No surprise was the fact that health care demand exploded after passage of the Medicare bill. Basically, free and unlimited health care was the driver behind the massive expansion in utilization. Within several years of passage, the federal government realized they had an out-of-control program on their hands. The wisdom of the day suggested that if this country could only train more doctors and build more hospitals, competition would increase and costs would decrease. Obviously, this was faulty economic thinking, so, instead, costs skyrocketed.

The last few decades of the twentieth century brought about many new regulatory programs to rein in the costs of health care. But in spite of such tactics as managed care, health maintenance organizations (HMO), and the scheme of reimbursement by diagnosis (diagnostic related group, or DRG, rather than specific treatments), health care costs continued to spiral out of sight in the latter part of the twentieth and first part of the twenty-first centuries.

The most recent debate on health care reform began shortly after the 2008 national election. Democrats controlled both houses of

Congress with wide majorities, as well as the White House.

Although 85 percent of the American public believed the economy and jobs were the most important problems facing the country during the recession of 2009, Congress elected to make health care the major debate of the session. The House of Representatives passed a sweeping health care reform bill in the summer of 2009, and the Senate eventually passed its bill on Christmas Eve. Both bills essentially passed along strict party lines with a significant number of House Democrats in opposition. Likewise, both bills passed by the absolutely slimmest majorities—218 votes in the House and 60 votes in the Senate to end debate, the bare minimum needed for passage.

Under the normal process for major social legislation, both bills would have gone to a House/Senate conference committee to work out differences and formalize the language. Then the conference committee bill would go back to each house for approval. After passage by both houses, the conference committee bill would go to the president to be signed into law.

However, between the Christmas Eve passage and the first conference committee meeting, Massachusetts held a special election to fill Senator Ted Kennedy's seat. Scott Brown, a Republican who ran against the proposed health care reform bills, was elected. This election reduced the number of Democrats in the Senate from 60 to 59. The Democrats at that point did not have enough votes to pass a conference committee bill, and, consequently, the House simply passed the unamended Senate bill. This was an example of politics at its worst. Up to that point, it had been unthinkable that Congress would pass major social legislation affecting one sixth of the U.S. economy on the narrowest of party-line votes.

The final bill as signed by President Obama was called the Patient Protection and Affordable Care Act (ACA), contains over 2,800 pages, and creates over 160 new government agencies and organizations. By contrast, the Medicare and Medicaid legislation contained less than 200 pages and passed with broad bipartisan majority support.

The main goal of the ACA is to decrease health care costs while providing universal health insurance. To date, the law has accomplished neither (see Chapter 9).

Over the past 120 years, elected officials in the United States have pushed the country closer to universal, nationalized health care. To date, this has been done in an incremental fashion, using the VA system, the Indian Health Service, Medicare, Medicaid, and now the Affordable Care Act.

With the best of intentions, supporters of these programs hoped they would stabilize the health care system, decrease costs, and ultimately provide health insurance for everyone. Unfortunately, but predictably, health care costs continue to rise and access to providers continues to decrease. The majority of Americans now have the sense that the system is broken.

# CHAPTER 2

# Who Uses
# Health Care Now?

Health care spending accounted for 18 percent of the U.S. economy, or $3.65 trillion in 2018. Moving, meaningful health care reform should not only solve the problem of providing insurance coverage, it should also consider who uses health care and at what cost.

The Agency for Healthcare Research and Quality (AHRQ) is a branch of the U.S. Department of Health and Human Services. The AHRQ conducts routine analysis of health care spending using the Medical Expenditure Panel Survey (MEPS), which is one of the most complete gatherings of national health care spending information available. The most recent data was released by AHRQ in November 2016 and provides numbers from 2014.[4]

The researchers looked at information from a specific year, 2014. The people who actually use health care and have expenditures are not the same individuals year after year.

Eighty-five percent of the U.S. population used health care in 2014. The top one percent of health care users accounted for 23 percent of total expenditures, at an average individual cost of $107,000. The top five percent accounted for 50 percent of expenditures, at an average individual cost of $47,000. The bottom 50 percent of users accounted for three percent of expenditures, at an average individual cost of $264.

The researchers also looked at expenditures by age group. Children under 18 years of age made up 23 percent of the U.S. population

---

4 "Concentration of health care expenditures in the U.S. noninstitutionalized popula-tion, 2014," by Emily Mitchell, Agency for Healthcare Research and Quality, November 2016 at https://meps.ahrq.gov/data_files/publications/st497/stat497.pdf

and accounted for ten percent of total expenditures. Young adults between the ages of 18 and 44 made up 35 percent of the population and accounted for 20 percent of health care expenditures. Individuals between the ages of 45 and 64 made up 26 percent of the population and accounted for 36 percent of expenditures. Seniors over the age of 64 made up 15 percent of the population and accounted for 34 percent of health care expenditures.

Not surprisingly, the data confirms that older people in general use many more health care services and consequently incur more expenditures than younger individuals. However, the data also shows that the top five percent of health care users 65 years of age and older accounted for 33 percent of expenditures. In the group under 65 years of age, the top five percent accounted for 50 percent of expenditures. This suggests that health care spending is more concentrated in a smaller percentage of patients in the younger population than in the senior group.

The AHRQ research shows that in any one year, a relatively small number of people use the majority of health care resources. These are not necessarily the same people year after year.

The most effective health care reform would allow the greatest number of people to participate voluntarily in the broadest insurance risk pool, using mandate-light or mandate-free catastrophic health insurance plans while providing subsidized high-risk pools for very high-cost users of health care.

These high-cost and high-users of health care and for people with pre-existing conditions, high-risk pools would provide coverage while holding down insurance costs for the vast majority of Americans.[5] There are various funding mechanisms for high-risk pools, but the important point is that they can isolate this small percentage of people who have high medical needs.

---

5    "Health care reform: lowering costs by putting patients in charge," by Roger Stark, MD, Policy Brief, Washington Policy Center, July 6, 2015 at http://www.washingtonpolicy. org/publications/detail/health-care-reform-lowering-costs-by-putting-patients-in-charge

The motivator for cost awareness in health care for patients as consumers would be to eliminate third-party payer systems and allow patients to control their own health care dollars, along with low-cost catastrophic insurance plans. This would increase competition, increase innovation at lower costs, assure quality, and improve access to services. It is arrogant for opponents of consumer empowerment to argue that people cannot become wise consumers of health care just as they are in other important areas of their lives.[6]

---

6    See Chapter 5 for a complete list of reform policies that put patients in charge of their own health care.

# CHAPTER 3

# Market Distortions Caused by the Third-Party Payer System

For the past 70 years, the United States has had a health care system in which patients receive health care, meet with doctors and receive hospital care, all while a third party, either an employer or the government, pays for the vast majority of health care costs. This "third-payer system" has disconnected patients as consumers of health care from the entity, an employer or government, that pays for that care.

Costs will continue to increase as long as each of us believes someone else will pay for our health care. Whether it is a government agency or an employer, a third party is now paying over 85 percent of health care costs, even as individual copays and deductibles increase. If we think someone else is picking up most of the cost, demand and utilization of health services will far outstrip supply. This is an immutable economic law, and it must be addressed before any reform will work.

Only when people can see the true costs and direct their own medical spending intelligently through a free market, will costs become transparent and likewise come under control. Critics of free-market reform say health care is too important and too complex to be left to the decisions of mere individuals. Yet health services are like any other economic activity, and because of their highly complex nature, they can only be managed through the unregulated interaction of providers and patients. No centralized plan, particularly one run by government, can account for all the factors involved.

For example, one of the largest health care expenditures is end-of-life care.[7] In 2014, 25 percent of Medicare spending was devoted to end-of-life care. Much of this spending was for expensive in-hospital care. If patients and their families controlled their own health care dollars, they would very likely make different decisions regarding end-of-life care, based on the individual needs and comfort of the patient.

The best motivator for providing cost awareness in health care for patients as consumers would be to eliminate third-party payer systems and allow patients to control their own health care dollars, along with access to low-cost catastrophic insurance plans. These changes would increase competition, increase innovation at lower costs, assure quality, and improve access to services. It is arrogant for opponents of consumer empowerment to argue that people cannot become wise consumers of their own health care, as people do in other important areas of their lives. No one would suggest that people should not make their own decisions about daily nutrition, housing, education, or marriage and family. The same should be true of health care.

7    "10 FAQs: Medicare's role in end-of-life care," The Henry Kaiser Family Foundation, September 26, 2016 at http://kff.org/medicare/fact-sheet/10-faqs-medicares-role-in-end-of-life-care/.

CHAPTER 4

# Considering Health Care
# as a Right

"We hold these truths to be self-evident, that all men are created equal, that they are endowed by their Creator with certain unalienable Rights, that among these are Life, Liberty and the pursuit of Happiness."

These words in the Declaration of Independence describe the "rights" of American citizens. They do not include health care. Yet, for over 100 years, some Americans have believed that health care is not only a right, but that the government should provide it and taxpayers should pay for it.

If medical treatment is a right, then what exactly does that mean? Does it mean that your neighbors, through the government, are obligated to provide all health care for you? Does it mean that anyone can demand the government pay for hospitalization, for prescription drugs, and for specialty treatments like organ transplants? Does it mean that every American has a right to the skill and knowledge of physicians and providers?

These questions lead to other questions. How does society pay for health care for all? Who gets to decide who should receive health care and how much? Who gets to decide what the health care budget should be? Who should have the power to make health care decisions for us?

Or rather than confront these issues, do proponents of health care as a right mean everyone should have health insurance? The problem with this belief is that simply having health insurance does not guarantee timely access to actual medical care. Every citizen of Canada has government-paid health insurance, but the long wait times for treatment, most notably for specialty care, would be unacceptable for Americans.

Everyone can agree that health care is a necessity of life. So are food, shelter, and clothing. Yet no one is demanding universal "food care" or universal government housing. The critical issue is that people expect access to food, shelter, and clothing. Americans expect choices and competition when they shop for these necessities of life.

The government exists to guarantee free markets for Americans when they seek access to virtually any product, but especially access to food, shelter, and clothing. No one would expect society, through government, to pay for these necessities of life for everyone.

If "food care" was controlled, paid for, and regulated by the government, we would have overutilization, fewer choices, and a limited supply. The private system of grocery stores and supermarkets guarantees access, choice, and competitive prices for everyone. The free-market system is efficient, voluntary, and fair.

The critical point is utilizing the best mechanism to allow the greatest number of Americans access to health care. The Canadian single-payer system does not guarantee timely access. The American experience with the Veterans Administration hospital system, a comprehensive government-controlled, single-payer health care program, reveals unacceptable wait times and huge inefficiencies. Fundamentally, these systems ration health care by waiting lists and limited money. The quality of care can vary.

Because of budgetary constraints, the demand for health care is much greater than the supply in virtually every country with a government-controlled health care system. As we have seen, even Medicare, essentially a single-payer plan, is not financially sustainable.

Just like in all other economic activities, the free market offers the best solution to provide the greatest access to health care and to control costs. People freely making their own health care decisions and using their own health care dollars would give Americans the best chance to utilize their "right" to access health care, with safety-net health programs provided for those who can't afford it.

At the end of the day, health care is an economic activity like any other, albeit with the most personal of interactions between patient and provider. Society should work toward putting patients in charge of their health care, reducing the role of government, and focusing on access, not health care as a supposed "right."

CHAPTER 5

# Buying Health Insurance

Every year millions of Americans buy auto, home, and life insurance from national companies in competitive marketplaces. People are savvy shoppers and have multiple choices when buying these types of insurance. Insurance is defined as "a practice or arrangement by which a company or government agency provides a guarantee of compensation for specified loss, damage, illness, or death in return for payment of a premium."[8]

Since the future is unknown, insurance is designed to mitigate risk. An insurance company sells policies to a large number of people who then comprise an insurance pool. If a bad event happens to a member of the pool, the insurance company pays that individual for the aspects of that event that are covered by the insurance policy out of the premiums paid by all the other members of the pool.

However, people often view health insurance differently than other types of insurance. When a person says he has "great health insurance," what he actually means is that his insurance covers nearly everything related to receiving health care, with essentially no out-of-pocket expense. Covered services can include dental treatment, eyewear, and routine visits to the doctor. This is analogous to a person having auto "insurance" that pays for routine maintenance services, including gas, oil, and brakes.

Obviously, the human body is different from a car or a house. However, from an insurance standpoint, which involves assessing and mitigating risk, health insurance is not fundamentally different from auto and home-owners insurance. The reasons health insurance should be understood as a way of assessing risk and preparing for

---

8   "Google dictionary," at https://www.google.com/search?rlz=1C1GGRV_enU-S751US751&q=Dictionary.

possible future events, and why this fact is important to the public debate, are discussed in this chapter.

## History of insurance in the United States

Benjamin Franklin formed the first insurance company in the United States in 1752 to compensate customers for fire damage to their homes. Growth of the insurance industry mirrored the expansion of the U.S. economy throughout the eighteenth and nineteenth centuries.[9] Unfortunately, a number of small, opportunistic, and underfunded insurance companies took people's money and then went out of business, leaving their customers uninsured.

In response to this problem, government regulation of the insurance industry began in the mid-1800s and varied from state to state. These regulations proved to be complex and ineffective. Insurance companies, dealing with large claims and increased competition, sought federal oversight of the industry to create consistency and stability in the sale of insurance.[10]

In 1868, the United States Supreme Court weighed in with its ruling in *Paul v. Virginia*. The plaintiff argued that a Virginia law requiring out-of-state insurance companies to post a large bond in order to do business in the state was illegal because it interfered with interstate commerce. The court upheld the Virginia law and thus gave states control over regulating the insurance industry. This ruling set the legal precedent for the next 80 years.

The sale of health insurance began in the early 1900s in the U.S. and within several decades was accepted and well established. Many of the early health plans were set up as pre-payment for major medical expenses, similar to current health maintenance organizations (HMOs).

---

9    "The history of insurance in America," by Andrew Beattie, Investopia at https://www. investopedia.com/ articles/financial-theory/08/american-insurance.asp.

10   "Insurance and antitrust law: The McCarran Ferguson Act and beyond, " by Alan Anderson, William and Mary Law Review, Volume 25, Issue 1, 1983, at http://scholarship. law.wm.edu/cgi/viewcontent.cgi?article=2189&context=wmlr.

By the mid-twentieth century, however, the insurance industry in general was consolidating and in many respects was becoming monopolistic. A second important U.S. Supreme Court decision, the 1944 *United States v. South-Eastern Underwriters Association*, re-examined the federal role in insurance regulation. Several insurance companies formed a six-state association, set pricing, and essentially formed a monopoly. The federal government sued the association.

The Supreme Court basically ruled that the sale of insurance did constitute interstate commerce and consequently could be federally regulated. The court went on to conclude that monopolistic associations such as the South-Eastern Underwriters violated the Sherman Antitrust Act and were further subject to federal oversight. This second court ruling led to mass confusion, and by some reports, chaos in the insurance industry. Companies that had lobbied strongly for federal oversight now viewed state control as the lesser of two evils.

### McCarran Ferguson Act

The insurance industry desperately sought clarification on regulatory oversight. Congress took up the issue and passed the McCarran Ferguson Act in March 1945. The law does several things. It gives states the power to tax and regulate insurance companies, gives state authority precedence over federal authority, and allows the use of the federal Sherman Antitrust Act only in cases of clear monopolistic behavior.

Members of Congress have understood the limitations that the McCarran Ferguson Act places on health insurance consumers. The U.S. House of Representatives voted in March 2017 to repeal the law with a bipartisan vote of 416-7.[11] Specifically, the House bill would have reinstated the potential for antitrust action while

---

11 "House passes McCarran Ferguson repeal bill," by Jennifer Webb, Insight + Analysis for the Independent Agent, March 23, 2017 at https://www.iamagazine.com/news/read/2017/03/23/house-passes-mccarran-ferguson-repeal-bill.

theoretically leaving states the control of the insurance industry. The impact of the bill would have been that health insurance companies could face both state and federal antitrust lawsuits. The U.S. Senate, however, has not yet passed repeal or reform of the McCarran Ferguson Act.

### Health insurance – exceptions to state regulation

Since 1945, states have retained control of the insurance industry in general. Health insurance, however, has some huge exemptions. Employer-paid health insurance falls under the federal ERISA laws and is not subject to state regulations.[12] Employers purchase health insurance in a private marketplace that is different from the individual and small group market. Half of all Americans receive their health insurance through their employer or their spouse's employer.

Medicare is a federal health insurance plan for seniors that began in 1965 and is heavily regulated by federal law. States can control supplemental and coinsurance, but Medicare is clearly a federal program. Fifteen percent of Americans are enrolled in Medicare.

Medicaid also began in 1965 and is a combined federal and state entitlement health insurance program for low-income people, the disabled, and people requiring long-term care. Although state taxpayers fund a substantial part of Medicaid, most regulations and control of the plan are under the federal government. The vast majority of enrollees have no out-of-pocket expenses. Twenty-three percent of Americans have Medicaid as their health insurance.[13]

The health uninsured rate is now between five to ten percent of Americans, which leaves five to ten percent of people in the individual health insurance market. From a health insurance

---

12   ERISA is the Employee Retirement Income Security Act of 1974.

13   "Medicaid – Statistics and Facts," by M. Mikulic, statista, October 26, 2018 at https://www.statista.com/topics/1091/medicaid/.

standpoint, it is this individual market that is subject to the McCarran Ferguson law.

## National marketplaces for insurance

Most Americans purchase auto and home-owners insurance from national companies, yet because of the McCarran Ferguson Act, companies are regulated by individual states. Every plan sold must conform to the laws and regulations of the state where the insurance is purchased. Pricing, however, can reflect the overall size of a company and the number of people nationally in the company's risk pool.

Auto and home-owners insurance have a good deal of uniformity across state lines. Pricing and compensation amounts may differ, but the required coverage mandates are very similar from state to state.[14] This is much different from health insurance, where special interest groups have encouraged state officials to expand the number of benefit and provider mandates included in plans.

## Mandates in insurance plans

The Affordable Care Act (ACA), or Obamacare, further entrenched government into the health care system in the U.S. Almost 40 percent of American citizens receive their health insurance through a government program, including Medicare, Medicaid, the Veterans Administration system, and now the ACA.[15]

Of all the government health care programs, the ACA goes the furthest in placing requirements on the insurance industry. Community rating, pre-existing conditions, no lifetime caps on

---

14    "GEICO home page," at https://www.geico.com/information/states/ca/, accessed November 20, 2017.

15    "Health care reform: lowering costs by putting patients in charge," by Roger Stark, MD, Policy Brief, Washington Policy Center, June, 2015 at https://www.washingtonpolicy.org/library/docLib/Stark-_Health_care_reform_and_alternatives_to_the_Affordable_Care_Act.pdf.

insurance payments, and the concept of children remaining on their parents plans until age 26 have all received a considerable amount of notoriety and contribute to the ever-rising cost of health insurance.[16]

Less publicized and less understood are the forced benefit mandates that the ACA requires in every health insurance plan sold in the U.S.

Prior to the ACA, states controlled the number of mandates in health insurance plans. For example, when the ACA became law, Washington state had a total of 58 mandates that had to be covered in every insurance plan sold in the state. Obamacare outlines ten broad benefit mandates that insurance plans must cover.

Mandates add to the cost of health insurance. On average, each mandate adds 0.5 to 2.5 percent to the overall plan cost.[17] Plus, the reality is that not everyone wants or needs each mandate. Why should a 27-year-old unmarried man pay for obstetrical coverage in his health insurance plan? Why should a non-drinker pay for alcohol rehabilitation?

The ACA has not provided universal health insurance because young and healthy individuals have not been willing to pay for costly plans that include benefits they don't want or need.

The solution for everyone is to deregulate the health insurance industry, eliminate costly mandates, and allow carriers to offer plans that patients, as consumers of health care, can actually use. Through market forces, let patients, not bureaucrats or special interest groups, tell insurance carriers what is desirable in policies.

Rather than forcing insurance companies to include special benefits, let patients use catastrophic/high-deductible plans coupled with health savings accounts for their health insurance needs.

---

16 "The Impact of National Health Care Reform on Washington State," by Roger Stark, MD, Policy Brief, Washington Policy Center, January 1, 2010 at https://www.washingtonpolicy.org/publications/detail/the-impact-of-national-health-care-reform-on-washington-state.

17 https://www.washingtonpolicy.org/publications/detail/update-on-health-insurance-mandates.

Although Blue Cross, Blue Shield, and private companies such as Aetna are national health insurance companies, their risk pools and pricing are set on a state or regional basis, not nationally.

Employers, especially large companies, can shop nationally for health insurance because of the federal ERISA laws. Although most employer plans are very generous, they are not subject to the specific health insurance mandates in any particular state.

Medicare and, to a lesser extent, Medicaid have greatly distorted the health insurance marketplace. It is impossible for private companies to compete against a government-owned monopoly. Consequently, there is no private market for health insurance for seniors and low-income Americans. Both Medicare and Medicaid give enrollees medical coverage with no, or very little, out-of-pocket payments from the enrollee.

Private insurance pays providers 75 percent more than Medicare pays.[18] Medicaid payments are even lower. The entitlement pays at most only 90 percent of what Medicare pays providers. These low government payments cause doctors, hospitals, and clinics to shift costs, in the form of higher prices, to individual and employer-paid insurers.

Medicare and Medicaid are financially unsustainable in their present forms. In an effort to salvage the programs, the government continues to decrease provider payments using various methods such as "quality of health care over quantity" and provider payments based on satisfactory (as determined by the government) outcomes.[19]

Employer-paid health insurance distorts the market as well.

---

18   "The growing difference between public and private payment rates for inpatient hospital care," by T.Selden, Z. Karaca, P. Keenan, C. White, and R. Krowick, Health Affairs, December 2015, at https://www.healthaffairs.org/doi/ abs/10.1377/hlthaff.2015.0706.

19   "Slumping Medicare margins put hospitals on precarious cliff," by Virgil Dickson, Modern Healthcare, November 25, 2017, at http://www.modernhealthcare.com/article/20171125/NEWS/171129969/slumping-medicare-margins-puthospitals-on-precarious-cliff.

Employees are isolated from the true costs of health care because their employer pays the majority of the insurance premium expense.

Consequently, 85 percent of Americans are in health insurance plans that involve a third-party as the payer. This is obviously a very different situation from auto or home-owners insurance, where individuals know to the dollar the true cost of their coverage because they find and pay for their own insurance. If someone else pays for a service, there is a high likelihood people will use more of that service than they would if they paid with their own money. They will also not be price-conscious and will not feel compelled to shop for the best deal, as they do with auto and home insurance.

CHAPTER 6

# Medicare

The federal Medicare and Medicaid programs became law in 1965. They have become two of the largest health insurance plans in the country and account for an ever-increasing share of federal and state taxpayer dollars. For the next 50 years, they will also require more public spending than any other government program, and they will add significantly to the national debt unless they are restructured and reformed. The survival of Medicare and Medicaid for future generations depends on patient-oriented reforms that must occur sooner rather than later to protect vital health services for patients.

Today, 40 percent of Americans are enrolled in these two programs. Because of retiring baby boomers and because of the expansion of Medicaid under the Affordable Care Act, the number of Americans in these two programs will undoubtedly increase.

At Medicare's outset in 1965, at least 60 percent of all seniors already had some form of health insurance. Also, low-income seniors were provided with health insurance on a voluntary basis through the Kerr-Mills law of 1960. These facts raise the questions of why a new program was needed, whether Medicare was simply pandering to the senior vote, and whether Medicare was being used as the first step to complete socialization of health care in the U.S.[20]

From the start, the cost of the Medicare program was grossly underestimated. The Health, Education, and Welfare Department told Congress in 1965 that the funding would require less than one percent of payroll taxes. By the late 1980s, however, this figure was increased to 1.6 percent and subsequently to 2.9 percent. In inflation-

---

20    "Medicare and Medicaid at fifty," by Roger Stark, MD, Policy Note, Washington Policy Center, February 2015 at https://www.washingtonpolicy.org/library/doclib/Stark-Medicare-and-Medicaid-at-50.pdf.

adjusted dollars, spending on Medicare was $4.6 billion in 1967 but had increased to $7.9 billion by 1971. This represented a 22 percent increase, whereas enrollment had increased by only six percent. By 1990, Medicare spending was nine times over its original budget.

In 2018, 60 million seniors received their health insurance from Medicare at a yearly cost of $750 billion.[21] With ten thousand baby boomers retiring every day, it is estimated that Medicare costs will explode in the next decade.

Medicare is set up in four parts, labeled Parts A through D. Part A covers hospital and other non-physician payments. It is financed through the 2.9 percent payroll tax, which has increased to 3.8 percent for high-wage earners since the Affordable Care Act (ACA) took effect in 2010.[22]

If all of Medicare deficits were to be covered, the payroll tax would have been raised to 18 percent in 2004, and to provide a break-even cash flow, each worker would have paid 20 percent in taxes in 2008. A payroll tax increase of this magnitude is not politically or economically possible, especially when stacked on top of worker income taxes. For this reason, Medicare remains unsustainable and cannot continue as currently structured.

Initially, only the first $6,600 of a worker's income was taxed to pay for Medicare. By 1993, Congress had increased the wage tax basis to $135,000, and the following year, this cap was eliminated completely so that all wages are now taxed in an attempt to cover skyrocketing Medicare expenses. And it is still not enough.

Like Social Security, Medicare was set up as a pay-as-you-go system, where today's benefits are mainly funded by current taxes.

---

21  "National Health Expenditure Fact Sheet," CMS.gov, 2018 at https://www.cms.gov/Research-Statistics-Data-and-Systems/Statistics-Trends-and-Reports/NationalHealthExpendData/NHE-Fact-Sheet.

22  The Affordable Care Act defines "high wage earner" as any individual who earns more than $200,000 per year or a couple that earns more than $250,000 per year. The 2017 tax reform legislation did not repeal the high-earner Medicare tax nor the high-earner tax on dividends and capital gains.

Obviously, the first wave of recipients had contributed nothing in payroll tax to the program. With the decreasing proportion of workers in future generations, and with the massive number of baby boomers approaching retirement, this pay-as-you-go system represents a financial catastrophe and is not viable.

Medicare Part B makes payments to physicians. Not surprisingly, Congress had no budget schedule for Part B. It was originally set up so that seniors would pay part and the federal government would match that to cover doctors' fees. In 1967, the total cost of Part B was $2 billion, but by 2000, the total expense was $90 billion a year. Taxpayers were funding 75 percent of that $90 billion instead of the originally proposed 50 percent match. Part B does include some degree of means testing, by which wealthier seniors pay a higher premium percentage than lower-income people.

Medicare Part C, or Medicare Advantage, began in 1997 and offers seniors essentially a health maintenance organization (HMO) insurance plan. For a set fee paid to a private insurance company, enrollees have most of their needed health care services provided. Part C is one of the fastest growing parts of Medicare.

Medicare Part D was added in 2003 and provides drug purchasing benefits to seniors who want a separate plan for pharmaceuticals.

The Johnson Administration's belief that increasing the number of hospitals and doctors would increase competition and bring costs down proved to be false logic. This economic model failed because officials did not consider that seniors do not spend their own money for the health care they receive; the bill is paid by a third party, the government. Not surprisingly, demand for relatively free health care went up sharply, and supply was increased as access was made easier. Increasing health care supply was only met with increasing demand. For example, the number of medical operations on seniors increased two and a half times in the first ten years of Medicare, in spite of a fairly constant rate of enrollment.

As with so many government bureaucratic programs, Medicare

is associated with a significant amount of cheating and waste. It is estimated that fraud, abuse, and waste together cost taxpayers at least $52 billion per year in improper payments alone.[23]

At least 20 percent of Medicare spending provides no benefit in lives saved or in improved quality of life for our senior citizens.[24]

Today, seniors are paying almost as much out of pocket for health care through their Medicare copays as they were for private insurance before passage of the Medicare bill. It is projected at current rates that seniors will be paying approximately 30 percent of their income for Medicare coverage by 2025.[25]

Since the late 1980s, the Center for Medicare and Medicaid Services (CMS) has been gradually decreasing hospital and physician reimbursements. Just like any other government wage-and-price control policy, supply is reduced, and seniors' access to health care services is now being restricted. In many communities throughout the nation, seniors are finding decreasing access to primary care because doctors cannot cover their office overhead cost with Medicare's low reimbursement payments. Clearly this restricts health care choices for seniors.

It should also be noted that Medicare law requires that if a physician accepts payment for a senior's health care from a source other than Medicare, that doctor can then not accept any Medicare patients for two years unless the patient is a federal employee. Because the private insurance market for seniors has essentially been eliminated in the U.S., even the wealthier elderly have no other option other than to participate in Medicare for major medical care. Doctors cannot accept cash or private insurance and still serve

---

23  "Medicare: Actions Needed to Better Manage Fraud Risks," U.S. Government Accountability Office, July 17, 2018 at https://www.gao.gov/products/GAO-18-660T.

24  "Waste, fraud and abuse in government health care," by Michael Cannon, Testimony before Congress, April 5, 2011 at http://www.cato.org/publications/congressional-testimony/wastefraud-abuse-government-health-care.

25  "Growth in Medicare and out-of-pocket spending: Impact on vulnerable beneficiaries," by S. Maxwell, M. Moon, M. Segal, The Urban Institute, 2000, pdf.

Medicare patients. It is ironic that a patient can offer to pay extra to the cab driver who takes him to a medical appointment, but offering extra money to a doctor is illegal.

Not only is Medicare nearly bankrupt now, but its financial future is actually much more dismal. With a proportionally decreasing labor force and an increasing number of seniors 65 and older, the Medicare pay-as-you-go system is on a course for fiscal disaster. Most young people in their twenties and thirties do not believe the program will exist for them when they reach age 65. The reality is that the payroll taxes paid by seniors during their working years account for, on average, only one-third of their individual Medicare utilization costs.[26]

The most recent Medicare Trustee report indicates that Medicare has grown from 0.8 percent of the gross domestic product (GDP) in 1974 to 3.5 percent in 2015. Future projections in the twenty-first century are for spending somewhere between six and nine percent of GDP. The trustees also report that the Medicare Trust Fund, or the plan's dollar reserves, will be depleted by 2030.[27]

The Affordable Care Act makes Medicare's funding problem worse. A large part of the payment for the ACA comes from financial cuts to Medicare. To limit future health care services under Medicare, the ACA directed officials to establish a non-elected committee, the Independent Payment Advisory Board (IPAB), to determine the "best practices" for providers. The IPAB theoretically could not use cost as a criteria for imposing limits, but for the panel to be effective in controlling costs, prices of tests and treatments would have to be considered. Fortunately, Congress repealed the IPAB in 2018. Medicare clearly needs reform, but the ACA reduces doctor and hospital reimbursement substantially.

---

26 "Social Security and Medicare Taxes and Benefits over a Lifetime," by C.E. Steuerle and C. Quakenbush, The Urban Institute, 2013.

27 "2015 Annual Report of the Boards of Trustees of the Federal Hospital Insurance and Federal Supplemental Insurance Trust Fund," pdf.

Although these planned doctor and hospital cuts may not ultimately happen, it is obvious that supporters of the ACA want to fund new entitlement programs by reducing doctor payments in Medicare even further. This policy change would make access to health care for seniors all the more difficult.

If Medicare is to continue in its present form, one or more of three changes must happen:

- Benefits will need to be decreased;
- Payroll taxes will need to be increased;
- Seniors will need to pay more out of pocket.

A fourth option, of course, would be to use general taxes to cover more of Medicare deficits. From an economic standpoint, none of these policies would predictably rein in the costs or decrease the demand for health care on the part of Medicare beneficiaries.

A number of government officials also believe increasing the productivity of doctors would make Medicare more efficient and would improve the program's financial status. Historically, the government has done nothing but increase the regulatory burden on providers, which has resulted in more inefficiency and waste.

It is somewhat unreasonable that people are calling for complete socialization of health care in the U.S. when Medicare, a socialized-medicine program itself, has been in such a dismal financial condition since its inception. By the mid-twenty-first century, Medicare expenditures will dwarf the yearly cost of Social Security.

CHAPTER 7

# Medicaid

There are currently four groups of people receiving assistance through the traditional Medicaid program that began in 1965. These are the poor, the disabled, low-income parents and children, and those individuals needing long-term care. Although parents and children make up most of the beneficiaries, long-term care accounts for 70 percent of Medicaid dollars spent.

Medicaid expenditures are the fastest-growing budget item for virtually all states, even though the federal government supplies, on average, 57 percent of all Medicaid dollars spent in the legacy program and at least 90 percent of dollars in the new ACA-expanded Medicaid program.

State reimbursement by the federal government for the traditional Medicaid is based on the wealth of the state, with poorer states receiving a higher percentage match of federal money than wealthier ones.

Physician participation is voluntary, and doctor reimbursement from Medicaid has always been lower than that of any other payer, including Medicare. Consequently, an increasing number of physicians are withdrawing from the program, thus decreasing beneficiaries' access to health care by limiting their physician choices.

The cost of Medicaid was $1 billion in its first year, exploding to $598 billion by 2018.[28] Twenty percent of Americans are enrolled in Medicaid, and over 50 percent of long-term care is funded by the program. By the year 2030, it is estimated that nursing home expenditures in Medicaid alone will equal the size of the entire Social Security program today.

---

28   See note 21.

The Medicaid entitlement has resulted in a number of harmful consequences. First, it discourages work and job improvement for low-paid employees because the increased income leads to workers losing their Medicaid benefits. It also encourages low-wage paying employers not to offer health benefits. They assume, or hope, taxpayers will provide those benefits. Medicaid also discourages private insurance companies from offering nursing-home policies, and this market shrinks further every year. Lastly, Medicaid discourages charity care and philanthropic work in the health care sector; if the government is already funding health care, donors are more likely to contribute money to other worthy causes.

The real tragedy for people in Medicaid is the program provides no better medical outcomes than having no insurance, except in very specific groups of patients such as high-risk pregnancies and people with HIV.

In 2008, Oregon lawmakers decided they had enough additional public money to put 10,000 more people on the state's Medicaid program. So, Oregon officials held a lottery that ultimately signed up 6,400 new Medicaid enrollees. A further 5,800 people were eligible for the program but were not selected in the lottery. People in this group had the same health and economic profile as the lottery winners, allowing researchers to make valid comparisons. This created the perfect test-case on the effectiveness of Medicaid in providing care compared to having no Medicaid coverage. These 5,800 people became the control group in an objective, prospective, randomized health care study.

It turns out that being put on Medicaid did not improve health outcomes, nor did it improve mortality statistics compared to having no insurance coverage at all. The Medicaid group had no improvement in the important objective measurements of blood sugar levels, blood pressure, and cholesterol levels. The study did find that vaguely defined "mental health" was improved; however, this was measured via subjective telephone interviews, not objective clinical data. For those few people requiring prolonged medical and hospital treatment, Medicaid did improve the financial status of those patients because their medical bills were covered by federal and Oregon taxpayers.[29]

State lawmakers unfortunately have been caught in a vicious cycle in which the more they spend on traditional Medicaid, the more money they receive from the federal government because of the 50/50 match. Lawmakers are rewarded with one federal dollar for every state dollar they spend.

The ACA required the federal government to pay for the entire Medicaid expansion for the first three years. Then states would pay ten percent of the expansion costs, starting in 2020. It is therefore no surprise that Medicaid is the largest, and fastest growing, budget item for almost all states in the country.

---

29   "The Oregon experiment – Effects of Medicaid on clinical outcomes," by K. Baicker, et. al., NEJM 2013; 368:1713-1722, May 2, 2013 at http://www.nejm.org/doi/full/10.1056/NEJMsa1212321.

CHAPTER 8

# The Public's Perception of Medicare and Medicaid

For meaningful reforms of Medicare and Medicaid to occur, it is important to understand the American public's perceptions of the programs now and in the future. A telephone survey by the Kaiser Family Foundation shows that 77 percent and 63 percent of those polled believe Medicare and Medicaid respectively to be "very important."[30]

For Medicare, 48 percent of poll respondents want funding to stay the same, but 41 percent want to see it increased. The numbers are similar for Medicaid at 47 percent and 37 percent respectively.

However, those polled were not too optimistic about Medicare's future. Only 44 percent of respondents were "somewhat" or "very" confident that Medicare would exist for future generations. The number dropped to 40 percent for respondents 18 to 54 years of age.

In other words, there is considerable inconsistency in how the public views Medicare. The vast majority of those polled believe we should spend at least as much, if not more, than we do now. Yet only a minority are confident that Medicare will be available in the future. Two thirds, or 68 percent, believe that "changes need to be made to Medicare" to sustain the program.

The most popular changes are negotiating drug prices with pharmaceutical companies, increasing premiums paid by wealthy seniors, and decreasing the amount paid to insurance companies. The most unpopular changes are increasing the eligibility age, increasing

---

30  "Medicare and Medicaid at 50," by M. Norton, B. DiJulio, and M. Brodie, The Henry J. Kaiser Family Foundation, July, 2015 at http://kff.org/medicaid/poll-finding/medicare-and-medicaidat-50/.

premiums for all seniors, and making deductibles higher. The vast majority, 70 percent, want to see a continuation of fixed benefits rather than a premium support or voucher system.

# CHAPTER 9

# The Affordable Care Act, Also Known as Obamacare

In March 2010, after 14 months of intense debate and with narrow partisan support and bipartisan opposition in Congress, President Obama signed major health care legislation into law. At no point in U.S. history has such broad, sweeping social legislation become law by such a slim political margin. The law remains extremely controversial and is at the center of much of the ongoing health care debate.

This wide-ranging law empowers the federal government to manage the health care of all Americans. The law has already generated thousands of pages of new federal regulations and multiple revisions.

The non-partisan Congressional Budget Office (CBO) originally estimated the law, once enacted, would cost $940 billion over the first ten years, from 2010 to 2019. Revenue to pay for the ACA was to come from a $500 billion cut in the Medicare entitlement program and $440 billion in new or expanded taxes.

The CBO estimate was based on ten years of revenue starting in 2010, but only six years of benefit payments starting in 2014. The most recent CBO projection was completed in 2016. The agency now estimates the ACA will cost $1.4 trillion over the next ten years, with offsetting revenue coming from cuts to the Medicare entitlement and taxes.[31]

After removing five percent for administrative costs to pay for the 160 new agencies and government organizations created by

---

31  "Federal subsidies for health insurance coverage for people under age 65: 2016 to 2026," Congressional Budget Office, March 24, 2016 at www.cbo.gov/publication/51385#-section1.

the law, the balance of the $1.4 trillion in spending is essentially being used to fund two programs: a huge expansion of the Medicaid entitlement program, and taxpayer subsidies for people to purchase health insurance in the newly created state and federally-run health insurance exchanges.

The law is based on an individual mandate that requires every adult in the United States over the age of 17 to have government-approved health insurance or else pay a penalty or tax. The tax began at $95 or 2.5 percent of a person's gross income (whichever was larger) per year in 2014 and rose to $700 or 2.5 percent of gross income per year in 2017. This tax was repealed by Congress as part of the major 2017 tax reform legislation. Individuals who do not have employer-provided or government-provided health insurance are forced to purchase their own individual insurance policy.[32]

In addition, the ACA requires employers with 50 or more employees to provide employee health insurance or pay a tax. There are various formulas, but essentially the tax is set at $2,000 per employee per year. Employers need to decide whether it is financially better to purchase employee health insurance or simply pay the tax. In July 2012, President Obama announced that enforcement of the employer mandate would be delayed by one year to January 2015, so it is now in effect.

Health insurance companies face many new regulations under Obamacare. The least politically controversial regulation requires a company to sell insurance to any person regardless of pre-existing health conditions. Essentially this means a person can wait until he becomes sick or injured before purchasing insurance. This concept is called guaranteed issue.

Another important regulation places everyone into a community-rated risk pool. There are small modifiers for age and smoking, but

---

32  "The impact of the Affordable Care Act in Washington State," by Roger Stark, MD, FACS, Policy Brief, Washington Policy Center, January 21, 2014, at www.washingtonpolicy.org/publications/ detail/the-impact-of-the-affordable-care-act-in-washington-state.

ultimately the law prohibits traditional insurance underwriting and requires that young and healthy people pay more and that older, sicker people pay less for similar health insurance.

The ACA requires that all health insurance policies must contain benefit mandates determined by government bureaucrats. Many of these mandates are beneficial, but each one adds to the cost of an insurance plan, and not everyone needs each of these mandates. For example, why should an unmarried 27-year-old man be forced to pay for obstetrical coverage?

The state and federal exchanges function as online insurance brokers through which individuals and small groups can buy health insurance with a federal taxpayer subsidy. Each exchange offers color-coded plans (bronze, silver, gold, and platinum) with various levels of costs and deductibles. To date, only 14 states, plus the District of Columbia, have set up exchanges.[33]

The federal government has assumed responsibility for running the exchanges for the residents in the other 36 states. Federal-taxpayer subsidies are provided in the exchanges for people earning between 138 and 400 percent of the federal poverty level (FPL) to help them purchase health insurance. Today, 400 percent of the FPL is a middle-class income, $103,000 for a family of four.[34] Approved rates and benefit packages in the various exchange plans are set by government regulators.

The most famous quote in support of the Obamacare bill came from Rep. Nancy Pelosi (D-12th District, California), then Speaker of the House, who said "...we have to pass the bill so you can find out what is in it..." This statement is an excellent reflection of the complexity of the law and the fact that many, if not most, of the Democratic members of Congress who voted for the ACA had very

---

33  "State health insurance exchanges: state run exchanges," Obamacare Facts, at www.obamacarefacts.com/state-health-insurance-exchange/.

34  "Federal poverty level," HealthCare.gov, at www.healthcare.gov/glossary/federal-poverty-levelFPL/.

little idea of what the law contained. All the Republican members of Congress opposed it.

President Obama told the American public that "if you like your current doctor, you can keep him; if you like your current health plan, you can keep it." These statements have proved to be grossly untrue, as insurance companies shift in and out of Obamacare exchanges and provider networks shrink. The number of people nationally who lost their health insurance is a moving target, but it runs into the millions.[35]

The experience in Washington state is informative. The Washington State Office of the Insurance Commissioner lists 470,000 people overall as newly insured since Obamacare became law.[36] However, the OIC reports a total of 837,500 people enrolled in the exchange plus the expanded Medicaid. This suggests that 367,500 (837,500 minus 470,000) Washingtonians lost their existing health insurance and were forced into either the Medicaid entitlement program or the state exchange.

The president also famously told Americans that the average family would "save $2,500 dollars per year on their health insurance premiums." The president's statement turned out to be untrue, and he later stopped defending it. Health insurance premiums have increased substantially in virtually every market, including large and small group employer-paid markets.[37]

To date, Obamacare has undergone 70 significant policy changes, including important deletions and delays. The Obama Administration unilaterally made 43 of these policy changes, Congress passed and

---

35  "How many people has Obamacare really insured?," by Scott Gottlieb, Forbes Magazine Online, May 14, 2015, at www.forbes.com/sites/scottgottlieb/2015/05/14/how-many-people-hasobamacare-really-insured/#6bbe2710777f.

36  "Uninsured rate in Washington state drops by half to 7.3 percent," Office of the Insurance Commissioner, Washington state, February 3, 2016, at www.insurance.wa.gov/about-oic/ newsroom/news/2016/02-02-2016.html.

37  "Here's how much your health insurance premiums could go up next year, they'll probably rise more than your income will," by Sy Mukherjee, Fortune Magazine Online, August 10, 2016 at www.fortune.com/2016/08/10/employer-health-premiums-rise/.

the president signed 24 policy changes, and the U. S. Supreme Court made three significant rulings on the original law.[38] Even the ACA's strongest supporters now admit the law was seriously flawed when it was enacted.

Congress passed a major tax reform bill in 2017. The new bill included the elimination of all the ACA taxes except the 0.9 percent increase in payroll taxes and the 3.8 percent dividends and capital gains tax on the wealthy. It is not clear where the funds to pay for the ACA will come from to offset this tax reform. The bill did repeal the individual mandate tax, making the constitutionality of the entire ACA questionable.

The recurring argument offered in support of the ACA is that 20 million people now have new health insurance.[39] When Obamacare was signed into law, 50 million Americans did not have health insurance for one reason or another.[40] The law's main goal was universal health insurance coverage. In this one important respect, the ACA has been a failure, since the law has provided coverage for only 40 percent of those previously uninsured.

Almost half of newly insured were put into the Medicaid entitlement program. As stated above, the most recent scientific study shows that Medicaid provides no better medical results than having no health insurance at all.[41] The fact that a person has health

---

38   "Constant changes highlight flaws in Affordable Care Act," by Roger Stark, MD, FACS, Policy Note, Washington Policy Center, May 17, 2016, at www.washingtonpolicy. org/publications/detail/ constant-changes-highlight-flaws-in-affordable-care-act.

39   "20 million people have gained health insurance coverage because of the Affordable Care Act, new estimates show," U.S. Department of Health and Human Services, HHS.gov, March 3, 2016, at www.hhs.gov/about/news/2016/03/03/20-million-people-have-gained-health-insurancecoverage-because-affordable-care-act-new-estimates.

40   "Obamacare's fifth anniversary," by Roger Stark, MD, FACS, blog, Washington Policy Center, March 25, 2015, at www.washingtonpolicy.org/publications/detail/obamacares-fifth-anniversary.

41   "The Oregon experiment – effect of Medicaid on clinical outcomes," by Katherine Becker, et. al., New England Journal of Medicine, May 2, 2013, at www.nejm.org/doi/full/10.1056/ NEJMsa1212321#t=article.

insurance is no guarantee of timely access to health care or to better clinical outcomes. This is especially true of the government's Medicaid program, which tends to underpay doctors for their time and services.

Another argument is that the ACA has slowed increases in health care spending. The rate of increase in health care costs has slowed, but this slowing began in the mid-2000s, well before Obamacare became law.[42] It is likely that the rising cost of health care would have moderated without passage of the ACA.

The U.S. Supreme Court has made three significant rulings on various parts of the ACA. The first case, *NFIB v. Sebelius*, was heard by the court in 2012 and essentially established the constitutionality of Obamacare.[43]

At issue was whether the government could force citizens to purchase a private product, in this case health insurance. The court ruled that the fine or penalty the ACA imposes for not purchasing insurance is actually a "tax" and that the constitution clearly gives Congress the authority to tax citizens.

In a second part of that case, the court ruled that the federal government cannot force states to expand the Medicaid entitlement program as written in the ACA. The court said each state can decide for itself whether to participate in the expansion without losing funding for its current Medicaid program.

The second case, *King v. Burwell*, dealt with the specific language of the ACA and whether people can receive subsidies in a federally established exchange, rather than a state exchange.[44] The court ruled

---

42  "Health care spending: historical trends and new directions," by Alice Chen and Dana Goldman, National Bureau of Economic Research (NBER), August 2015, at www.nber.org/papers/w21501. pdf.

43  "National Federation of Independent Businesses, et. al. v. Sebelius, Secretary of Health and Human Services, et. al.," Supreme Court of the United States, October Term, 2011, at www. supremecourt.gov/opinions/11pdf/11-393c3a2.pdf.

44  "King, et. al. v. Burwell, Secretary of Health and Human Services, et. al.," Supreme Court of the United States, October Term, 2014, at www.supremecourt.gov/opinions/14pdf/14-114_qol1.pdf.

in 2015 that even though the ACA specifically says "…exchange established by the State," the intent was that any government exchange could be used, including a federally created exchange. The effect of the ruling was to amend the law, without changing its wording, to expand the federal-subsidy program to states that did not have their own exchanges.

Republican attorneys generally have sued the federal administration over the constitutionality of the law now that there is no "tax" or penalty for not owning health insurance. The case is currently working its way through the court system and may ultimately be heard by the U.S. Supreme Court.

Liberals and conservatives alike agree that rising health care costs are unsustainable and that any meaningful health care reform must address this problem. Obamacare has been a dismal failure in reducing or slowing the rise in health care costs. USA Today compiled data from the Obama Administration and reported that for 2016 in the ACA exchanges cost of the average family deductible soared. Premium increases have leveled off somewhat recently. However, to hold down costs, insurance companies are now contracting with specific doctors and thereby limiting provider networks.

In Mississippi, average family premiums shot up 42 percent, and in South Carolina, they increased 37 percent. In North Carolina, annual premiums and deductibles for the most commonly purchased family plans increased on average by about 20 percent. Alaska had the biggest average premium increase among states—35 percent— for a typical 27-year-old male.

Three other states—Minnesota, Montana, and Hawaii—saw annual cost increases of more than 30 percent. In Washington state, the average premium increased by 13.5 percent.[45] The national average increase for premiums in 2017 was estimated at 24 percent.

---

45  "13 health insurers file 154 plans for 2017 – 13.5 average requested rate changes," Office of the Insurance Commissioner Washington State, May 16, 2016, at www.insurance. wa.gov/about-oic/ newsroom/news/2016/05-16-2016.html.

Twenty-nine states have fewer gold plans and five states are losing more than half of their gold plans.[46]

Half of all Americans receive health insurance through their employer or a spouse's employer. Even in the employer-based market, health insurance premiums are increasing much faster than general prices reported in the consumer price index (CPI). Fortune Magazine Online reports that the CPI is increasing at about one percent per year, whereas on average, employer-paid health insurance premiums are increasing at 6.5 percent per year.[47] The average family plan with employer-paid insurance now costs $18,000 per year, which is $4,400 more than the average cost before the ACA was enacted.

Costs continue to rise in the two other large government insurance programs. Almost 40 percent of Americans are now enrolled in Medicare or Medicaid entitlement plans. The Congressional Budget Office reports that Medicare spending will double by 2026 to $1.29 trillion annually and that federal Medicaid spending will increase by 75 percent to $621 billion over the same time period.[48]

In spite of the fact that Obamacare is costing the country billions, if not trillions, in public dollars, private health care costs continue to rise for individuals and families.

Although 20 million Americans are insured through the ACA, 30 million people are still without health insurance. Many of these uninsured are young and healthy individuals. They have made a conscious economic decision not to pay for expensive health insurance containing benefit mandates they do not want or need.

---

46 "State by state data show bigger 2016 exchange premium, deductible jumps," by Jayne O'Donnell, USA Today, December 16, 2015, at usatoday.com/story/news/ nation/2015/12/16/state-state-datashow-bigger-2016-exchange-premium-deducti- ble-jumps/77353890/.

47 "Here's why you'll likely pay more for your employer-sponsored health insurance," by Laura Lorenzetti, Fortune Magazine Online, June 21, 2016, at fortune.com/2016/06/21/ health-carerising-costs/.

48 "CBO: Medicare spending up this year," by Ron Shinkman, Fierce Healthcare, August 25, 2016, at www.fiercehealthcare.com/finance/cbo-says-medicare-spending-up-year.

Especially with the pre-existing conditions clause in Obamacare, younger and healthier people feel it makes more sense to pay the government penalty for not having insurance and wait until they become ill to purchase needed health coverage.

As noted, only 14 states plus the District of Columbia have established their own ACA exchanges. Elected leaders in the other 36 states have declined to participate in this provision of Obamacare, and the federal government has created an exchange for their residents. Most state exchanges, for example the one in Washington state, are theoretically set up to be self-sustaining financially.[49] Members of the Washington State Exchange Board, however, admit that financial assistance may be needed from "other" public resources, presumably a reference to getting money in the state general fund.

The number of insurance companies participating in the exchanges is trending downward nationally. Some states have a fairly stable number of carriers. However, the national average of companies participating in the exchanges has dropped from 6.5 in 2016 to 5.8 in 2017.[50] The number of counties across the country with only one insurance company selling coverage increased to 18 percent in 2017, up from two percent in 2016.[51]

This sharp decrease in consumer choices reflects the imbalance in the risk pool in the exchange markets. The majority of enrollees are older and sicker individuals. The architects of Obamacare estimated that the exchanges would need young and healthy people to make up at least 40 percent of all enrollees in order to be financially viable.

---

49   "Washington Health Benefit Exchange, Report to the Washington state legislature, December 1, 2012, at www.wabexchange.org/wp-content/uploads/2015/08/391423087296_Legislation_120112_ Sustainability_Report.pdf.

50   "Analysis of 2017 premium changes and insurer participation in the Affordable Care Act's health insurance marketplaces," by Cynthia Cox, et. al., The Henry J. Kaiser Family Foundation, July 28, 2016, at kff.org/health-reform/issue-brief/analysis-of-2017-premium-changes-and-insurerparticipation-in-the-affordable-care-acts-health-insurance-marketplaces/.

51   Ibid.

That number is currently only 28 percent nationally, far below the number needed to make ACA exchanges work.[52]

Many state exchanges are now at risk of closing. The governor of Kentucky wants to put his state's exchange into the federal exchange.[53] The commissioner of Tennessee's Department of Commerce recently reported that because of increasing premiums and decreasing insurance company participation, the Tennessee exchange is "very near collapse."[54] States that close their exchanges, of course, can push their residents into the federal exchange. This puts federal taxpayers at greater risk, not only for increased premium subsidies, but also for the higher overhead costs of running the exchanges.

The ACA expanded Medicaid coverage, the entitlement program for the poor, to any person between the ages of 18 and 64 who earns less than 138 percent of the federal poverty level. The federal government paid 100 percent of the expansion cost through 2016 and then will gradually decrease that amount to 90 percent starting in 2020. As noted, the U.S. Supreme Court ruled that states can decide whether or not to expand Medicaid and, as of the end of 2018, 36 states plus the District of Columbia have elected to expand Medicaid.[55]

Nationally, approximately 50 percent of the newly insured people under the ACA were placed in the Medicaid entitlement program.[56] The percent varies by state, and for Washington state, according to the Office of the Insurance Commissioner (OIC), over 80 percent

52    "What, me buy insurance?," by Bob Herman, Modern Healthcare, May 14, 2016 at www. modernhealthcare.com/article/20160514/MAGAZINE/305149980.

53    "Bevin gives Kynect a temporary reprieve, by Baylee Pulliam, Louisville Business Journal, July 13, 2016, at www.bizjournals.com/louisville/news/2016/07/13/bevin-gives-kynect-a-temporaryreprieve.html.

54    "Obamacare is 'very near collapse' in one state," by Bob Bryan, Business Insider, August 24, 2016, at www.businessinsider.com/obamacare-near-collapse-in-tennessee-2016-8.

55    "A 50-state look at Medicaid expansion," FamiliesUSA, February 2016, at familiesusa. org/ pro duct/50-state-look-medicaid-expansion.

56    Ibid.

(680,000 out of 837,500) of people newly insured under Obamacare were put in the Medicaid expansion.[57]

Without significant change and reform, the existing Medicaid program is not financially sustainable.[58] Adding over ten million new enrollees to the entitlement program has made its financial status even more precarious. One out of five Americans nationally and one out of four Washingtonians are now in the Medicaid entitlement program.

Medicaid pays providers roughly 40 percent of what private insurance pays. Consequently, access to care for existing Medicaid patients is poor, especially in primary care. Adding millions of new patients to Medicaid will make this access problem worse. Doctors, clinics, and hospitals have little incentive to accept more Medicaid patients when government policy means they lose money on every visit.

The real tragedy for patients is, except for very specific diagnoses, having Medicaid insurance provides no better clinical outcomes than being uninsured.[59]

Consumer Operated and Oriented Plans, known as CO-OPs, were placed in the Affordable Care Act as a compromise for lawmakers who wanted a "public option" health insurance plan. The stated goal of CO-OPs is to increase competition and consumer choice in the health insurance exchanges by creating government-sponsored competition against private insurance companies. CO-OPs must comply with all state insurance laws, mandates, and regulations.

---

57  "Uninsured rate in Washington state drops by half to 7.3 percent," Office of the Insurance Commissioner, Washington state, February 3, 2016, at www.insurance.wa.gov/about-oic/ newsroom/news/2016/02-02-2016.html.

58  "Medicare and Medicaid at fifty," by Roger Stark, MD, FACS, Policy Note, Washington Policy Center, September 3, 2015, at www.washingtonpolicy.org/publications/detail/ medicareand-medicaid-at-fifty

59  "Obamacare's fifth anniversary," by Roger Stark, MD, FACS, blog, Washington Policy Center, March 25, 2015, at www.washingtonpolicy.org/publications/detail/obamacares-fifthanniversary.

Initial funding was provided through two types of federal government loans given at favorable interest rates. Start-up loans must be repaid to taxpayers within five years and solvency, or reserve, loans must be repaid within 15 years. Essentially, CO-OPs are tax-supported start-up health insurance companies with limited financial reserves.[60]

A total of 23 CO-OPs were established and received $2 billion in federal taxpayer funds. Most went bankrupt, and, to date, only several remain solvent.[61] Hundreds of thousands of enrollees have been forced to find new health insurance, and taxpayers have lost billions of dollars.

The ACA requires a payment model for providers that ultimately will eliminate the solo or small group practitioner. The policy goal is to shift from fee-for-service payments for doctors and hospitals to a global payment model in which all providers are paid with a single check for any given patient. This forces doctors to become hospital employees or to form some type of financial relationship with hospitals or large physician groups.

The central planners of Obamacare call these relationships accountable care organizations (ACOs).[62] These basically function like the unpopular health maintenance organizations (HMOs) of the late 1980s and early 1990s. HMOs are effective at holding down health care costs, but they do this by rationing care for patients using a gatekeeper system. Patients and doctors grew very dissatisfied with

60    "Consumer operated and oriented plans (CO-OPs) and the Affordable Care Act," by Roger Stark, MD, FACS, Legislative Memo, Washington Policy Center, February 22, 2014, at www. washingtonpolicy.org/publications/detail/consumer-operated-and-oriented-plans-co-ops-and-theaffordable-care-act.

61    "Another Obamacare co-op folds, leaving only 6 remaining," by Ali Meyer, FoxNews Politics, September 13, 2016, at www.foxnews.com/politics/2016/09/13/another-oba-macare-co-op-foldsleaving-only-6-remaining.html.

62    "Changes in patient and doctor relationships in United States health care," by Roger Stark, MD, FACS, Policy Note, Washington Policy Center, November 1, 2015, at www. washingtonpolicy.org/ publications/detail/changes-in-patient-and-doctor-relationships-in-united-states-health-care.

them 30 years ago, and, understandably, their popularity waned. Even with a goal of "better quality," ACOs are a merely a repeat of the failed HMO model.

Because of the new payment model and the significant cuts to Medicare, hundreds of hospitals, mostly located in rural areas, are at risk of closing.[63] Some estimates show that 30 percent of the 2,000 rural hospitals in the U.S. are likely to close for financial reasons in the next few years because of diminishing payments.

In addition to taxes, financial cuts to Medicare, the entitlement program for seniors, were used to pay for a large percentage of Obamacare costs.[64] In the original budget, the CBO determined that $500 billion of the $940 billion total cost of the ACA would come from Medicare. Most of these cuts were to come from the provider side of the program—that is, further reductions in payments to doctors, hospitals, ambulance services, nursing aid, and kidney dialysis units.

Medicare currently pays providers approximately 70 percent of the amount that private insurers pay. Because doctors have trouble paying their expenses with these lower reimbursements, they limit the number of Medicare patients they are financially able to see. The Obamacare cuts to Medicare will make this access problem for seniors worse.

Neither Congress nor the Obama Administration were aggressive about making these cuts. This was anticipated by the architects of the ACA. Consequently, the law established a non-elected committee called the Independent Payment Advisory Board (IPAB) that would recommend the "best practices" in the Medicare program. These best

---

63  "With hospitals in critical condition, can rural America survive?," by Mattie Quinn, Governing the States and Localities, July 2016, at www.governing.com/topics/health-human-services/govrural-hospitals-critical-condition.html.

64  "The impact of the Affordable Care Act in Washington State," by Roger Stark, MD, FACS, Policy Brief, Washington Policy Center, January 21, 2014, at www.washingtonpolicy.org/publications/ detail/the-impact-of-the-affordable-care-act-in-washington-state.

practices theoretically could not be determined by cost. In reality, however, the committee would be charged with holding down the expenditures in Medicare.

Congress voted to repeal the IPAB in 2018, putting to rest the entire debate over the "death panel" issue.

The ACA is one of the most complex and sweeping laws ever passed by Congress. The law and its many amendments run to 2,700 pages, plus thousands of newly added regulations. Health care makes up 18 percent of the U.S. economy, and Obamacare touches virtually every part of the health care delivery system. Not only the individual health insurance market, but also the employer-paid market, Medicare, and Medicaid are affected by the ACA.

The government-imposed benefit mandates in all insurance plans, the insurance regulations of community rating and pre-existing conditions, and the expansion of Medicaid all contribute to the rising costs of health care in the United States. Even the financial cuts to Medicare that pay for Obamacare simply transfer taxpayer money from the senior insurance program to the ACA.

CHAPTER 10

# Other Government Programs

## The Veterans Administration

The Department of Veterans Affairs (VA) is the second largest department in the federal government, serving nine million veterans and with a budget of $200 billion per year.[65] Currently, the VA is a true socialized medicine program, with the government owning the hospitals and employing the doctors and staff. In one form or another, the department has been active since the Revolutionary War.

Quality and timeliness of care are not uniform in all VA facilities. Scandals have plagued the organization. Privatization of parts or all of the system have been debated for years in an effort to improve services.[66] Because of the unique needs of combat veterans and because of widespread popular support, the VA system will remain in place for the foreseeable future.

## The Children's Health Insurance Program (CHIP)

The Children's Health Insurance Program (CHIP) is a joint federal and state insurance plan for children whose families earn too much money for Medicaid eligibility.[67] CHIP began with bi-partisan

---

65    "We can fix veterans' health care without privatizing it," by N. Schlichting, The Washington Post, April 2, 2018, at https://www.washingtonpost.com/opinions/we-can-fix-veterans-health-care-without-privatizing-it-heres-how/2018/04/02/3b85a448-3443-11e8-8bdd-cdb33a5eef83_story.html?utm_term=.dbf96600ab24.

66    "Trump Administration plots costly private-care expansion for veterans," by Isaac Arnsdorf, Pro Publica, Inc., November 15, 2018 at https://www.propublica.org/article/trump-administration-plots-costly-private-care-expansion-for-veterans.

67    "The Children's Health Insurance Program (CHIP)," healthcare.gov, at https://www.healthcare.gov/ medicaid-chip/childrens-health-insurance-program/.

support as an amendment added to the federal Balanced Budget Act of 1997.[68]

Congress originally funded the program for ten years. CHIP was reauthorized and expanded significantly in 2009 under the Obama Administration and a Democratic Congress. The last funding reauthorization occurred on January 22, 2018, and will run for six years.[69]

President Clinton made an attempt at enacting universal health insurance during his first term in office. This plan was rejected by Congress. CHIP is a result of Congress's inability to pass government-run, universal health care in 1993. U.S. Senate leadership, specifically Senator Kennedy (D-MA) and Senator Hatch (R-UT), strongly believed that it was the government's responsibility to at least provide health insurance for all children except those from wealthier families.

CHIP is set up similarly to the Medicaid program in that the funding is provided through a combination of federal and state taxpayer dollars. Unlike Medicaid where the funding is 50 percent federal money and 50 percent state money, the federal government pays on average 70 percent of the costs of CHIP. These federal funds are capped, again unlike Medicaid under which the more a state spends, the more the federal government matches that spending. Patient eligibility under CHIP goes up to 19 years of age.

States have some latitude in organizing CHIP. In 36 states, the program is separate from Medicaid. In 49 states, CHIP may or may not be separate but does fund some Medicaid patients, and in 19 states, CHIP covers health care for some pregnant women.[70]

---

68 "Children's Health Insurance Program overview," National Conference of State Legislatures, January 2017, at http://www.ncsl.org/research/health/childrens-health-insurance-program-overview.aspx.

69 "Status of federal funding for CHIP and implications for states and families," Kaiser Family Foundation, January 2018, at https://www.kff.org/medicaid/fact-sheet/status-of-federal-funding-for-chip-andimplications-for-states-and-families/.

70 "Medicaid and CHIP eligibility, enrollment, renewal, and cost sharing policies as of January 2017: Findings from a 50 state survey," by T. Brooks, et. al., Kaiser Family Foundation, January 2017, at https://www.kff.org/medicaid/report/ medicaid-and-chip-eligibility-enrollment-renewal-and-cost-sharing-policies-as-of-january-2017-findings-from-a-50-state-survey/.

CHIP is more flexible than Medicaid. States are allowed to make their own plans, can tailor the benefit packages as needed, can institute cost sharing or a monthly premium (capped at five percent of the family's yearly income), and can control the eligibility requirements. In general, well-child doctor visits and most dental procedures are "free" (funded by taxpayers) for CHIP recipients.

Although the program is taxpayer-funded, many state officials believe that CHIP is "a non-entitlement."[71] It is separate from Medicaid, although eligibility requirements are the same as Medicaid with the exception that income criteria are more relaxed and range between 300 and 400 percent of the federal poverty level (FPL).[72] This level is $77,250 to $103,000 of income a year for a family of four people in 2019.[73] Medicaid's income limit for eligibility is considerably lower.

CHIP has become a mid-income entitlement. For example, a total of 800,000 children in Washington state are in Medicaid. An additional 50,000 children are in CHIP.[74] One out of every two kids in Washington state is either in the Medicaid or the CHIP government-run health program.

Funding for CHIP can be confusing. Looking at Washington state as an example, in 2016, total spending for CHIP was $162

---

71    "Washington Children's Health Insurance Program (CHIP)," BENEFITS.GOV, at https://www.benefits.gov/benefits/ benefit-details/1615.

72    7 "Medicaid and CHIP income eligibility limits for children as a percent of the federal poverty level," State Health Facts, Kaiser Family Foundation, January 2017, at https://www.kff.org/health-reform/state-indicator/medicaid-and-chipincome-eligibility-limits-for-children-as-a-percent-of-the-federal-poverty-level/?currentTimeframe=0&selectedRows =%7B%22states%22:%7B%22washington%22:%7B%7D%7D%7D&sortModel=%7B%22colId%22:%22Location%22,%2 2sort%22:%22asc%22%7D.

73    "Federal poverty level," HealthCare.gov, 2019, at https://www.healthcare.gov/glossary/federal-poverty-level-FPL/.

74    "Gov. Inslee calls for Congress to reauthorize CHIP: Facts about Apple Health (Medicaid) and children," Washington State Health Care Authority, September 2017, at https://www.hca.wa.gov/about-hca/gov-inslee-calls-congressreauthorize-chip-facts-about-apple-health-medicaid-and-children.

million.[75] This number needs some clarification, however. The federal government has allowed 11 states, including Washington state, to transfer federal CHIP money over to their Medicaid program for children of families earning more than 133 percent of the FPL. The actual total of federal dollars that came into Washington state in 2016 for CHIP was $219 million. State officials then transferred $57 million over to the Medicaid program and devoted the remaining $162 million to CHIP. In this way, Washington state officials diverted federal CHIP money to subsidize the state's Medicaid program.

The Children's Health Insurance Program is essentially an extension of the Medicaid entitlement for families that earn too much money to qualify for basic Medicaid. Advocating for children's health is politically popular, and, consequently, CHIP has enjoyed bipartisan support since its beginning in 1997.

There is no question that taxpayer-funded health insurance has helped some children and adults. The policy question is why a family that earns almost $103,000 a year cannot find private health insurance at a reasonable cost, especially to cover children. The answer is that government regulations and benefit mandates have increased the price of private health insurance to unaffordable levels for millions of American families. Instead of being able to purchase affordable, high-quality health insurance in a truly free and open market, families are forced to buy expensive insurance that government bureaucrats, not consumers, believe is best.

In addition, CHIP and Medicaid crowd out private insurance. If the government provides "free" or low-cost health insurance, the private market is undercut and cannot compete. Such aggressive price competition would normally be illegal in the private market.

---

75 "Total CHIP expenditures," State Health Facts, Kaiser Family Foundation, 2016, at https://www.kff.org/medicaid/ state-indicator/total-chip-spending/?currentTimeframe=0&selectedRows=%7B%22states%22:%7B%22washington%2 2:%7B%7D,%-22virginia%22:%7B%7D%7D%7D&sortModel=%7B%22colId%22:%22Federal%20Share%22,%22sort%2 2:%22desc%22%7D.

Researchers do not agree on the exact amount of crowd-out, but they do agree that it occurs. The published range is somewhere between ten and 60 percent.[76]

The Children's Health Insurance Program is simply another intrusion of government bureaucrats into the U.S. health care system. It has made the third-party payer problem worse, as more families are denied access to their own choices in affordable health coverage. It is one more gradual step toward a single-payer, socialized government-run plan—a concept Americans have repeatedly rejected since the 1930s.

A safety net is needed to cover the most vulnerable children, but middle-income families should be able to find high-quality, affordable health insurance in a competitive, private market.

---

76 "Addressing Crowd-Out," Georgetown University Health Policy Institute Center for Children and Families, Georgetown University, March 2009, at http://ccf.georgetown.edu/wp-content/uploads/2012/03/Addressing-CrowdOut.pdf.

CHAPTER 11

# Changes in Patient and Doctor Relationships

The relationship between patients and doctors is one of the most personal of any professional interactions. Yet this relationship is progressively and relentlessly being eroded by government regulation. With the best of intentions and with a high level of compassion, Americans have gradually allowed government officials to control our health care delivery system, and now we are experiencing those relationship changes.

Until World War II, patients paid doctors on a fee-for-service (FFS) basis, just as they would pay other professionals, such as lawyers, architects, and auto mechanics for their services. Few people had health insurance. During the war, the government imposed strict wage and price controls on the economy, but officials did allow employers to pay for employee health insurance as a way of supplementing capped wages.

This policy was the beginning of a health care system in the United States in which a non-involved third party, in this case the employer, paid doctors for medical services provided to employees and their families. The government further entrenched this third party employer-paid model by allowing employers to deduct the cost of employee health benefit expenses from their corporate taxes. Doctors were still paid on a fee-for-service basis, either by employers directly or by employers through insurance companies.[77]

In 1965, the government became directly involved as a third-party payer in the U.S. health care system when Congress passed the

---

77   "History of health insurance benefits," Employee Benefit Research Institute, March 2002, at http://www.ebri.org/publications/facts/index.cfm?fa=0302fact.

Medicare and Medicaid entitlement programs. Medicare is socialized health care for seniors, paid for by payroll taxes on workers, the federal general fund, and individual premiums. Medicaid, at least in theory, is a safety-net insurance plan for low-income people and the disabled. It is paid for by state and federal taxpayers who, of course, are the same people. Doctors have traditionally been paid on an FFS basis in both entitlement programs.[78]

Government officials further involved themselves in health care relationships when Congress passed the Affordable Care Act (ACA), or Obamacare, in 2010. The ACA expanded Medicaid and gives taxpayer subsidies to middle-income people to induce them to buy health insurance through state and federal insurance exchanges.[79]

The vast majority of health care in the U.S. is now paid for by a third party, either employers or government officials. Demand and spending on health care have exploded, which is consistent with the economic principle that utilization of a product or service will increase dramatically if consumers believe someone else is paying.

By the mid-1980s, the government was no longer a disinterested third-party payer, simply paying health care bills as they arrived. To cover exploding costs in Medicare, Congress increased worker payroll taxes, raised premiums, and devoted more money from the federal general fund. In addition, elected officials directed more taxpayer money on both the federal and state levels into the Medicaid program.

Doctors were still paid on a fee-for-service basis for the care and medical skill they provided to patients, but state officials started ratcheting down Medicaid payments. The federal government began to control Medicare payments using wage controls for doctors and

---

78   "History, Medicare and Medicaid," Centers for Medicare and Medicaid Services at http://www.cms.gov/About-CMS/Agency-Information/History/index.html?redirect=/History/.

79   "History and the timeline of the Affordable Care Act (ACA)," eHealth, October 22, 2014, at https://www.ehealthinsurance.com/resource-center/affordable-care-act/history-timeline-affordable-care-act-aca.

a complex system called diagnosis-related group (DRG) for hospital payments.[80]

Government officials use the DRG system to pay hospitals a bundled or fixed amount of money for a specific patient diagnosis or operation, not based on actual services provided to an individual patient. There are modifiers for complications and extended lengths of stay, but, essentially, hospitals that are more efficient and have fewer patient complications do better financially.

Officials gradually decreased doctor payments from Medicare from the late 1980s until 1997. Part of the Balanced Budget Act of 1997 was a Medicare payment model for doctors called the sustainable growth rate (SGR). The SGR fixed doctor payments to target rates of health care spending growth and compared that growth to changes in the national gross domestic product (GDP).

If health care costs decreased or stayed constant in relationship to GDP, doctors would get more money. If costs rose, they would get less. Not surprisingly, health care costs continued to rise. Congress subsequently amended the SGR 17 times to guarantee that doctor reimbursements would not decrease.[81] These temporary "doc fixes" caused uncertainty and anxiety among physicians.

In 2015, with bipartisan support, Congress passed a permanent "doc fix" called the Medicare Access and Children's Health Insurance Program Reauthorization Act (MACRA). It replaces the SGR with more stable payments to doctors, provided they meet government-mandated rules.

Unfortunately, Congress did not provide a meaningful funding source, so MACRA will add $141 billion to the federal debt over the next ten years and $500 billion over the next 20 years. In other words, what has been hailed as a great bipartisan

---

80    "Diagnosis-related group," Health Law Resources at https://www.healthlawyers.org/hlresources/Health%20Law%20Wiki/Diagnosis-related%20group%20(DRG).aspx.

81    "Sustainable growth rate (SGR) summary," American College of Physicians, pdf.

solution to doctor payments is really just the current Congress passing debt and tough budget decisions on to future lawmakers and ultimately taxpayers.[82]

MACRA also discourages FFS and promotes alternative payment models. The ultimate goal of MACRA is to only pay doctors who practice in accountable care organizations (ACOs) or medical homes. These are simply the new names for traditional health maintenance organizations (HMOs). They essentially require doctors and hospitals to join in some type of financial partnership. From experience since the 1990s, HMOs can control costs through a gatekeeper rationing system, but patients have been very dissatisfied.

The ACA also encourages the use of ACOs and medical homes and further expands their use.[83]

What all these changes mean for patients is a gradual, but definite, shift in the U.S. health care system. We are already seeing these changes, and they are coming at a more rapid rate. The doctor in solo practice or in a small group will eventually disappear. For financial stability and to decrease government-required paperwork, doctors will be employed by hospitals or will have to join large physician groups. Hospitals will merge to form ever larger entities.

Ultimately, the FFS model will disappear in health care, although it will remain the primary way consumers pay for all other professional services. "Quality" will become the new buzzword, and providers will be paid based on government-dictated criteria. This concept, called pay-for-performance (P4P), has already begun. The meaning of "performance," however, will be decided by public officials. Quality

---

82  "Fix the flawed Medicare doc fix," by John Graham, National Center for Policy Analysis, Report No. 364, April 2015, pdf.

83  "The care transformation: What's the difference between CI, ACO and PCMH?," by Sarah O'Hara, The Advisory Board Company, September 24, 2014 at https://www.advisory.com/ research/care-transformation-center/care-transformation-center-blog/2014/09/deciphering-thereform-alphabet.

and payment method will be determined by government bureaucrats, not by patients.[84]

Many people would argue that since the government is paying for health care, it has the right and the responsibility to dictate what care people can receive and how much providers will be paid. This, of course, leaves patients out of the decision-making process and completely changes the intimate and personal relationship patients have with their doctors. Americans deserve a better health care system.

The most important person in the health care system is the patient, not cost-conscious employers or distant budget-driven government bureaucrats. The patient, as a consumer of health care, should determine the value and quality of services received and how much doctors should be paid to provide them. Market forces, not the government, should drive the relationships between patients and providers.

Moving away from the third-party payer interference that started in the 1940s and widening the range of available and affordable consumer-based choices in health care would re-connect people with providers and show that policymakers respect the close private relationship that exists between patients and their doctors.

---

84 "Pay-for-performance," by Julia James, Health Affairs Health Policy Briefs, October 11, 2012 at http://www.healthaffairs.org/healthpolicybriefs/brief.php?brief_id=78.

# CHAPTER 12

# The Looming
# Doctor Shortage

I t is the year 2030. A retired couple moves to a different state and cannot find a doctor who has time to see new Medicare patients. A poor family enrolls in Medicaid health insurance but cannot find a primary care physician who can fit new patients into his or her busy schedule. A worker in a rural area has excellent private health insurance but must drive hundreds of miles to receive medical care.

Are these gloomy scenarios possible or even probable?

The United States in general and most states in particular will face a severe doctor shortage in the next ten to 15 years. Not only is the population growing, but the baby boomer generation is aging and will require more medical services in the near future.

The advantage of a free market is that resources are constantly adjusted and balanced so that supply consistently equals demand. As demand fluctuates, supply will increase or contract to meet the market's needs. In health care, demand is set by the patients, and supply is a function of the number of doctors and their availability. The government has imposed central planning on both the demand and the supply side of our health care system.

The American Medical Association (AMA) was formed in the mid-nineteenth century to represent physician concerns in the United States. In 1904, the AMA created the Council on Medical Education (CME) to set standards for medical training. Up to that point, medical education in the U.S. had no uniform curriculum. School quality ranged from an excellent, formal education all the way to diploma mills that provided very little training in how to practice medicine.

The CME recruited the Carnegie Foundation to review existing medical schools and to make recommendations for improving quality. The results were published in 1910 and became known as the Flexner Report, named for the lead author.[85] The Flexner Report standardized medical education, but as quality improved, so did the cost of training doctors. The report recommended state oversight of medical schools. State legislatures were then placed in charge of building new schools, and the state also had the authority to regulate school class size.

Prior to 1905, there were 161 medical schools in the U.S. producing about 5,400 graduates a year. By 1922, the number had decreased to 81 schools turning out just 3,000 doctors annually. The number of schools dropped further to 66 in 1935, although class enrollment increased again to 5,400 students graduating as doctors.[86]

Controversy about the necessary number of medical graduates raged during the 1930s and early 1940s. The federal Committee on the Costs of Medical Education believed there were too few graduates, whereas the Commission on Medical Education felt there were too many new doctors coming out of school. The AMA opposed any new medical schools.[87] From 1945 to 1956, the number of graduates expanded to 8,250 per year, but only two new schools were built.

In 1959, the federal government issued a study, the Bane Report, which recommended increasing the number of medical schools and using federal taxpayer subsidies to assist the building and management of the schools. The federal government gradually increased funding for new and existing schools. The AMA continued to oppose the building of new institutions.

By 1965, however, with the passage of Medicare and Medicaid,

---

85   "Medical Education in the United States and Canada A Report to the Carnegie Foundation for the Advancement of Teaching," by Abraham Flexner, The Carnegie Foundation for the Advancement of Teaching, 1910, online at www.ia600308.us.archive.org/22/items/medicaleducation00flexiala. pdf.

86   "Medical Schools and Their Applicants: An Analysis," by Richard A. Cooper, Health Affairs, 22, no.4, (2003):71-84.

87   Ibid.

medical educators, organized medicine, and politicians struggled with a looming doctor shortage. Consequently, medical school output was doubled from 1965 to 1980 when 18,200 students graduated. A total of 44 new traditional, allopathic medical schools, plus ten osteopathic schools were constructed from 1960 to 1980, the first major increase since 1920.[88]

In 1976, the federal government declared the doctor shortage was over, and by 1979, there were reports of a "doctor glut." Yearly medical school output has essentially been flat for the past 40 years, even though the U.S. population increased 37 percent over the same period.

There are now 129 accredited allopathic, or traditional, medical schools in the U.S. The country also has 25 accredited osteopathic schools that combine traditional medical education with advanced study of the musculoskeletal system. Every student must pass the United States Medical License Examination after graduating, and all states require separate licensing with variable reciprocity. There are currently one million physicians in the U.S., with 48 percent in some type of primary care (family practice, internal medicine, pediatrics, and obstetrics and gynecology) and 52 percent in specialty practice.[89]

According to the Association of American Medical Colleges (AAMC), there are currently 110,000 post-graduate residency positions in the U.S. Although Congress placed a limit on taxpayer funding in 1997, these residency hospitals rely heavily on federal taxpayer money. This money comes out of the Medicare program and last year totaled $16 billion.[90] Training programs that emphasize primary care are prioritized.

---

88   Ibid.

89   "Professionally Active Physicians," Kaiser Family Foundation, March, 2019 at https://www.kff.org/other/state-indicator/total-active-physicians/?currentTimeframe=0&select-edRows=%7B%22wrapups%22:%7B%22united-states%22:%7B%7D%7D%7D&-sortModel=%7B%22colId%22:%22Location%22,%22sort%22:%22asc%22%7D.

90   "Federal Support for Graduate Medical Education," Congressional Research Service, December 27, 2018 at https://fas.org/sgp/crs/misc/R44376.pdf.

Many patients in the U.S. have access to care from doctor extenders, medical professionals in training who do not hold doctor licenses. There are now over 75,000 physician assistants (PAs) in practice.[91] Our country also has the services of 168,000 nurse practitioners (NPs).[92]

The supply of doctors is augmented by people from other countries coming to the U.S. to practice medicine. Between 15 percent and 20 percent of all residency positions are now filled by foreign medical graduates (FMGs).[93]

The Association of American Medical Colleges (AAMC) anticipates a shortage of 150,000 doctors in the next 15 years. Other sources predict a shortage of 200,000 doctors by 2025.

The AAMC is advocating for a 30 percent increase in medical school enrollment, which would result in approximately 5,000 additional new physicians graduating each year.[94]

Population and policy trends show the U.S. is now facing a tsunami of health care demand. The baby boomer generation is reaching the age of high medical use. In addition, the Affordable Care Act has added millions of previously uninsured patients to our health care system. When increasing demand is not accompanied by increasing supply, access to health care will become a problem, and waiting lists will become commonplace.

Surveys reveal that 86 percent of existing medical schools plan to increase enrollment.[95] The AAMC found that 12 existing schools recently added 150 students, and four new schools added a total of 190 students.[96]

---

91   "Projected Number of Physician Assistants in Clinical Practice,2010," The Kaiser Family Foundation StateHealthFacts.org, at statehealthfacts.org/comparemaptable.jsp?ind=773&cat=8.

92   "Total Nurse Practitioners, 2010," statehealthfacts.org, The Kaiser Family Foundation.

93   Ibid.

94   "Shortage of Doctors an Obstacle to Obama's Goals," by Robert Pear, The New York Times, April 26, 2009.

95   "Medical School Enrollment Plans: Analysis of the 2007 AAMC Survey," aamc.org.

96   Ibid.

The cost of a medical education is extremely high. Students at a public medical school pay, on average, $49,000 per year for tuition, books, room and board. The average cost at a private medical school is now $67,000 per year. The median debt students have at graduation is $150,000 at a public school and $180,000 at a private institution.[97]

The demographics of medical students are changing. In the past 30 years, the number of women entering the medical field has increased dramatically. Many graduating classes now contain at least 50 percent women, a substantial increase from the five to ten percent seen a generation ago. Women are more inclined to enter specialties with fixed hours and are more likely to take time off for childbirth and care. The quality of students entering medical school is now as high as ever, but there are concerns that as the government encroaches more on health care, the best and brightest will seek other careers.

It is extremely expensive to build a new medical school. Texas did a recent study and found that a new school with a modest class size of 60 students (240 in four years) and a faculty of 170 would cost $92.6 million over six years with a onetime capital cost of $65 million.[98]

Receiving the proper accreditation is also a problem. The Liaison Committee on Medical Education, sanctioned by the U.S. Department of Education and Congress, must approve any new medical school. The accrediting process takes, on average, eight years.[99]

This government-planned, third-party payment system has created ingrained market distortion and has caused an excessive demand in health care. After all, when someone else pays, there is no incentive for patients to question the price or quantity of

97   "How Much Does Medical School Cost?," by Tara Kuther, Ph.D., About.com Guide, 2010.

98   "Basic Steps to Establish a New Medical School," Texas Higher Education Co-ordinating Board, September, 2008 at www.thecb.state.tx.us/reports/PDF/1515,PD-F?CFID=22430987&CFTOK EN=51275481.

99   "Overview: Accreditation and the LCME," Liaison Committee on Medical Education at www. lcme.org/overview.htm.

services that are consumed in their care. Economic law says that in this situation, prices will soar and goods and services will be heavily overutilized.

For years the government has also controlled the number of medical schools, the number of graduates from these schools and their licensure. This has created a further distortion in the supply of health care. Government central planners are now even attempting to legislate not only the total number of doctors, but also the number of primary care physicians and the number of specialists in the country. This is as futile and absurd as the government telling people how many laptop and desktop computers we need. No amount of information or analysis will enable central planners to know how many doctors, and of what type, the country needs.

Only through balanced market forces, ones that allow patients to control their own health care dollars, can the demand be correctly determined. The necessary and sufficient number of doctors each community needs can only be known through millions of routine, voluntary actions made in the free market.

The following policy recommendations can guide policymakers in making sure the nation produces a sufficient number of doctors to serve the needs of patients in the years ahead.

1. Allow the health care market, not central planners, to determine the number of doctors needed.
2. Remove employers and government (except for safety-net programs for the most needy) from health care financing and allow patients to control their own health care dollars.
3. Allow independent medical schools without the mandatory high overhead of accompanying medical research.
4. Allow medical schools to determine their own enrollment and graduation numbers.
5. Encourage the use of long-term, low interest rate loans for medical students.

6. Encourage the use of physician extenders—physician assistants and nurse practitioners—to make the delivery of quality health care more efficient.
7. Increase the use of well-trained foreign medical graduates and reduce their visa/immigration requirements.
8. Encourage the use of community scholarships for medical students with guaranteed commitments to service in the community after graduation.
9. Foster innovative health care delivery methods such as convenient walk-in clinics and personalized concierge practices.
10. Remove government from the licensing process and use private rating agencies or professional specialty organizations for competency determinations and to maintain physician quality.

# CHAPTER 13

# Drug Pricing and the Food and Drug Administration

## Drug Pricing

There is a great deal of confusion and misunderstanding in the United States about drug pricing, manufacturing, marketing, and the impact of government regulations. This confusion has been made worse by the recent egregious behavior of several pharmaceutical manufacturers that raised the prices of some drugs by up to 5,000 percent.[100]

There is a growing opinion that the government should place a price ceiling on drugs. In 2014, prescription drug costs accounted for 9.8 percent of overall health care expenses.[101] In economics, setting price limits on goods and services always results in scarcity, with fewer of the price-controlled products being produced and made available to consumers. This has been confirmed by the disastrous centrally planned economies of communist countries. Similar distorting effects and shortages would occur if government officials sought to control prescription drug prices.

Only seven percent of possible drugs survive the research phase, make it through clinical trials, and go on to be marketed and make money for their manufacturers.[102] Over 90 percent of

---

100 "Here's why Turing Pharmaceutical says 5,000% price bump is necessary," by Laura Lorenzetti, Fortune Health, September 21, 2015 at http://fortune.com/2015/09/21/turing-pharmaceuticals-martin-shkreli-response/.

101 "Health expenditures," Centers for Disease Control and Prevention, October 7, 2016 at https:// www.cdc.gov/nchs/fastats/health-expenditures.htm.

102 "Success rates for experimental drugs falls: study," by Bill Berkrot, Reuters, February 14, 2011 at http://www.reuters.com/article/us-pharmaceuticals-success-idUS-TRE71D2U920110214.

research on new drugs loses money and fails to produce treatments. The final pricing of the few successful drugs must make up for all the money spent on the research and development (R&D) of all the previous failures.

In 2015, the ten largest drug manufacturers spent 18 percent of their total revenue on R&D.[103] A better comparison across industries is the percent of sales spent on R&D. According to the National Science Foundation, in 2014, the average of profit from sales across all industries spent on R&D was 3.5 percent. The pharmaceutical industry spent 13.4 percent of total profit from sales on R&D, a higher percent than the computer and electronic industry, which spent 10.2 percent.[104]

Drug companies are criticized for their large advertizing budgets. However, research shows that there is a substantial range for what pharmaceutical manufactures spend on marketing. In 2013, the ten largest drug companies spent between 17.9 percent and 28.4 percent of total revenue on advertizing.[105] The average was 23 percent. Compare those levels with the 20 percent that Oracle and Microsoft spend on marketing their products. The company Salesforce actually spends over 50 percent of its revenue on marketing.[106]

Just as professional athletes receive large salaries because of their time-limited careers, innovative drug manufacturers have a limited amount of time to earn a profit on a drug before its patent expires. Once a drug goes "off patent," it must compete with generic drugs. Generic

---

103 "Top 50 pharmaceutical companies by prescription sales and R&D spending in 2015," The Statistics Portal, 2016 at https://www.statista.com/statistics/273029/top-10-pharmaceuticalcompanies-sales-and-rundd-spending-in-2010/.

104 "Businesses spent $341 billion on R&D performed in the United States in 2014," by Raymond M. Wolfe, National Science Foundation, August 25, 2016 at https://www.nsf.gov/statistics/2016/nsf16315/.

105 "Pharmaceutical industry gets high on fat profits, " by Richard Anderson, BBC News, November, 2014 at http://www.bbc.com/news/business-28212223.

106 "What percent of revenue do publically traded companies spend on marketing and sales?", by Sarah Brady, Vital Designs.com, 2015 at https://vtldesign.com/digital-marketing/content-marketing-strategy/ percent-of-revenue-spent-on-marketing-sales/.

manufacturers have a definite role in the health care system and can offer good prices, but they do not have the added expense of R&D. The sale of generic drugs cannot fund the discovery of new pharmaceuticals.

Government price controls not only limit the supply of a product, they also limit the interest of financial investors in a company. Fewer investors mean less money for life-saving new drugs and less competition in developing those drugs.

Over the past few years, the increased spending on prescription drugs has largely been due to the increased use of drugs for very special and rare diseases. The Department of Health and Human Services recently released a study that found that specialty drugs accounted for one percent of all prescriptions, but 32 percent of all prescription drug costs.[107]

The high prices of these new and special pharmaceuticals must be weighed against the cost of treating a patient without that drug. For example, Sovaldi is a drug that treats hepatitis C and costs $84,000 for a curative three-month treatment. The alternative, a liver transplant, costs over $500,000 and is associated with a great deal of pain and suffering, assuming a healthy donor liver is even available.[108] Though it appears expensive in terms of price, Sovaldi is much more affordable than the alternative.[109]

Manufacturers do not set the final price of their drugs. Pharmaceutical pricing goes through a series of steps before drugs actually reach patients. Depending on whether people buy their drugs directly from a pharmacy or through their insurance, several transactions and multiple layers of profit are built into the system.

In general, manufacturers sell to wholesalers who then sell to

---

107 "Prescription drugs: innovation, spending and patient access," U.S. Department of Health can Human Services, December 7, 2016 at http://delauro.house.gov/sites/delauro.house.gov/files/Prescription-Drugs-Innovation-Spending-and-Patient-Access-12-07-16.pdf.

108 "Sovaldi costs less than other treatments," by F. Jason Harris, Modern Healthcare, May 1, 2014 at http:// www.modernhealthcare.com/article/20140501/NEWS/305019929.

109 Of course in economic terms, the death of a patient is an even cheaper outcome. This raises important ethical concerns not addressed in this policy paper.

pharmacies. Most, if not all, insurance companies use pharmacy benefit managers (PBMs) to negotiate the best pricing from manufacturers. Drug wholesalers and PBMs provide a service, but this comes at an added cost to the consumer. Wholesalers and PBMs will argue that they obtain better prices from manufacturers, but these contracts and the supposed benefits are not transparent. Actual contract pricing and rebates are usually closely guarded and not readily available to the public.

What is known is that PBM companies, in general, have higher profit margins than drug manufacturers.[110] Drug wholesalers and pharmaceutical benefit managers may have a role in the drug market, but only if they add value for patients. Their contracts and pricing should be transparent so consumers can decide the amount of value added.

If public officials really want to bring prices down and increase competition in the drug industry, they should focus on streamlining the government drug approval process to decrease the time and money manufacturers devote to bringing a new drug to market. Depending on the study, the average cost of bringing a drug to market today is $2.5 to $5 billion and takes ten to 15 years to get through the government regulatory process.[111] There is even a backlog of generic drugs awaiting government approval.[112]

Putting price controls on drugs would not solve the fundamental problem of our health care delivery system. Unlike the electronics or computer markets, in health care, a third party, either the government through Medicare, Medicaid, and Obamacare, or an employer through

---

110 "Profits in the 2016 Fortune 500: Manufactures vs. wholesalers, PBMs, and pharmacies," by Adam J. Fein, Drug Channels, June 21, 2016 at http://www.drugchannels. net/2016/06/profits-in-2016-fortune-500.html.

111 "Cost to develop new pharmaceutical drug now exceeds $2.5 B," by Rick Mullen, Scientific American, November 24, 2014 at https://www.scientificamerican.com/article/ cost-to-develop-new-pharmaceuticaldrug-now-exceeds-2-5b/.

112 "FDA still struggling with backlog of generic drug applications," by Ed Silverman, STAT Pharmalot, March 2, 2016 at https://www.statnews.com/pharmalot/2016/03/02/ fda-generic-drugs/.

insurance companies, pays for the majority of health care in the United States. Drug wholesalers and pharmaceutical benefit managers may negotiate better drug pricing, but this comes at a cost that is not readily transparent. Patients, as consumers of health care, and doctors as providers, are isolated from the actual costs of drugs and treatments.

Throughout our economy, a vigorous and creative free market, without third-party interference, results in better products at cheaper prices every day with constant improvement. Allowing patients, in consultation with their providers, to decide which drugs are best clinically and financially for them should be the goal of health care reform, not damaging price controls.

## Food and Drug Administration

One of the most regulated areas of health care spending in the United States is drug development and sales.

This is overseen by the Federal Drug Administration. In 1965, it took approximately two years to develop a new drug and get it through FDA approval at a cost of $4 million. By 1989, it took three years at a cost of $231 million. As stated above, today it takes $2.5 billion to $5 billion with an approval time of greater than 15 years.[113]

As the FDA ramped up more regulations through the 1970s, with increasing costs to the drug companies and long processing times, the number of new drugs dropped by almost 60 percent. Obviously, this hurt hundreds of thousands of patients who could have been helped by new drug development. Although the numbers are difficult to obtain, it is estimated that between 21,000 to 120,000 patients per decade die because of FDA regulations. This is at an estimated cost of $42 billion per year. On the flip side, FDA regulations are estimated to prevent 10,000 deaths per decade at most.[114]

---

113 See note 107.

114 "The Patient-Centered Solution; Our Health Care Crisis, How It Happened and How We Can Fix It," by Roger Stark, MD, available through amazon.com.

In the 20 years from 1975–1995, the number of clinical trials mandated for every new drug doubled and the number of patients required in each trial tripled.

The increasing cost and time of the FDA approval process means that medicines with low profit margins, that treat few patients, and which treat rare diseases are not even being developed or brought to market.

CHAPTER 14

# Fixing the Broken
# Mental Health System

The treatment of mentally ill patients has undergone radical changes in the past 150 years, and not always for the better. Care is fragmented and places a huge social burden on American communities. Unfortunately, public-health treatment remains grossly underfunded. But that hopefully is about to change.[115]

The U.S. House passed H.R. 2646 to make the federal government accountable, on an outcomes basis, for the $130 billion spent annually on mental-health treatment. Multiple mental-health organizations and media outlets support the bill, called the Helping Families in Mental Health Crisis Act.

The U.S. Senate passed similar legislation, and President Obama signed the compromise bill into law, making mental-health treatment a government priority.

People with mental illnesses range from well-functioning individuals to those with severe disabilities. The role of government is to serve as a safety net and to help dysfunctional, impaired people who may do harm to themselves or others.

Institutionalizing the mentally ill became popular in the mid-nineteenth century, and the federal government funded psychiatric hospitals, or asylums. Community and home-based treatment began in the 1950s and was placed into federal law in 1963 with the Community Mental Health Centers Construction Act.

Federal action caused existing psychiatric hospitals to rapidly

---

115 "The role of government in fixing the broken mental health system," by Roger Stark, MD, Washington Policy Center at https://www.washingtonpolicy.org/publications/detail/the-role-of-government-in-fixing-the-broken-mental-health-system-2.

close. From 1955 to 1995, the number of institutionalized patients dropped by 90 percent, and many of these mentally ill people became homeless. For example, from 1955 to 2000, the number of psychiatric beds per 100,000 people in Washington state plummeted from 339 to 22. There is now a shortage of available psychiatric beds both nationally and in Washington state.

Community-based treatment over the past 60 years has included regional mental-health centers, supervised residential homes, psychiatric teams, and improved medications. Research shows that both institutionalization and community treatment can be effective, depending on the patient's specific needs. Both approaches have supporters among mental-health professionals.

The tragedy is that both treatment methods are underfunded by federal, state, and county governments. Just like basic services, such as police, fire, and emergency, the fundamental role of government here is the treatment and protection of the mentally ill. Unlike other areas of health care where patients can make rational choices and direct their own care, providing quality mental treatments for those with no other option is a public-health issue and should be a government priority.

Studies confirm that 40 percent of patients with severe psychiatric problems have been incarcerated at some point in their lives. Many patients had been waiting weeks, or even months, in jail before receiving a professional mental examination, let alone caring and constructive treatment for their conditions.

There has been a tragic and growing trend in the use of regular hospital emergency rooms for "psychiatric boarding" or "warehousing." This is not only costly but, more importantly, can exacerbate the patient's mental problem.

Because of the psychiatric-bed shortage, many mentally ill people wind up back on the streets, living homeless and abandoned. This is one reason that simply building more subsidized housing does not solve one of the root causes of homelessness. The government is currently placing a huge financial burden on regular hospitals, county and city jails, and state prisons by not allocating sufficient resources to caring for the mentally ill.

The fact that elected officials now recognize the underfunding problem is a promising start to effectively treating mental illnesses. This is good public policy and will immediately make our communities safer. It will help reverse the mistakes of the past and benefit the state prison system, hospitals and, most importantly, people living with mental illnesses.

# CHAPTER 15

# Vaccines

n 1965, the United States government assured that all children
would receive access to vaccines for common childhood diseases
through the passage of the Vaccination Assistance Act.[116] The law
created a program that provides federal grants to local authorities for
preventive health services, including immunizations.[117]

Nearly three decades later, the federal government expanded the
plan by creating the Vaccines for Children (VFC) program, enacted
as part of the Omnibus Reconciliation Act of 1993.

Today, routine child vaccinations have greatly reduced the
incidence of death, disease, and suffering among children and
brought immense social and economic benefits to the nation.
However, the financial infrastructure of this valuable program
is not sustainable and has led to severe market inefficiencies.
Manufacturers in general are not reimbursed enough to make it
worth their while to produce vaccines, leading to a supple-versus-
demand mismatch.

Childhood vaccinations are essential to public health. Fundamental
policy changes are needed to secure the long-term stability of the
country's immunization program, promote the efficient and cost-
effective use of vaccines, and ensure that government financial
disincentives do not burden the practice of medicine or inhibit the
development of new vaccines.

---

116 Public Law 87-868, "The Vaccine Assistance Act of 1962, to assist states and communities to carry out intensive vaccination programs designed to protect their populations, particularly all preschool children, against poliomyelitis, diphtheria, whooping cough, and tetanus,"
enacted October 23, 1962 and added as Section 317 to the Public Health Services Act.

117 2 "Childhood Vaccines: Challenges in Preventing Future Shortages," by Janet Heinrich, Subcommittee on Public Health, Committee on Health, Education, Labor, and Pensions, United States Senate and the General Accounting Office, 2002.

The reasons that some states have low vaccination rates can be divided into three separate yet related categories. These are:

- Reluctance of parents to vaccinate their children;
- The state's low reimbursement rate to doctors;
- Underutilization and waste of vaccine doses.

Resolving the doubts of parents about the safety and importance of child vaccinations has been overlooked by many health officials and is a growing problem. This may be due to the increasing publicity about the perceived dangers of vaccines and their unproven association with causing autism.[118] A further reason is the ease of enrolling children in public school without their being immunized.

The American Academy of Pediatrics has long held that the reimbursement rate for vaccine administration is too low. According to a report by the Immunization Congress, some pediatricians and many family practice doctors are seriously considering ending their vaccination services. Almost half of the physicians surveyed reported that their practice had deferred obtaining specific vaccines for purely financial reasons, and that for many private practices, "providing childhood vaccinations is increasingly a losing financial proposition."[119]

Higher payments are necessary to cover providers' additional effort and time spent educating hesitant parents on the value of vaccines. Growing parent reluctance is partly an outcome of the surge of information (and misinformation) distributed on the Internet and other social media. For example, the supposed "danger" of autism as a side effect of vaccinations has required an immense amount of doctors' time to correct.[120]

---

118 "Strategy to Improve Immunization Rates in Washington," Washington State Department of Social and Health Services, Report to the Legislature, 2008.

119 "Immunization Puts Mounting Financial Pressure on Physicians," by Crystal Phend, Medpage Today, Vaccines, December 1, 2008, at www.medpagetoday.com/InfectiousDisease/Vaccines/11948.

120 "Suspicion of vaccines spurs debate, worry; Public health officials fear consequences of forgoing shots," by Paul Nyhan, Seattle Post Intelligencer, March 16, 2009, at www.seattlepi.com/local/403719_vaccine16.html.

A predictable consequence of "free" government-provided vaccines is that doctors are not incentivized to use them judiciously. Neglect, underutilization, and over-ordering of vaccines have led in some cases to waste and misplaced medical resources.[121]

As currently designed, the Vaccines for Children program is not stable or sustainable. The federal government now purchases over half of the childhood vaccines in the country. Because of the government's massive purchasing power, manufacturers are forced to take a 60 percent reduction in reimbursement for vaccines, compared to what the private sector pays, leading to artificial cost shifts that can double the market price of the medicine. For example, Merck sells the measles-mumps-rubella (MMR) vaccine to the CDC for $18.26 a dose, while charging a private patient $46.54 for the same dose.

The policy of steep discounts for public vaccination programs is intended to save the government money, but it is false savings because the strong financial disincentive to drug firms has led to severe distortion in the vaccine manufacturing market. The production and research of vaccines is no longer profitable for many pharmaceutical companies, and many of them have left the market.

Fifteen years ago, more than ten medical research firms in the United States were studying and producing vaccines for children; today, only four firms do this work.[122] Furthermore, the majority of the eight basic vaccines recommended for children today are produced by a single company.[123] The result is a less stable supply of vaccines for both the government and private patients, and a reduction in the

---

121 "More than 20,000 Oregonians urged to get new vaccinations," by Andy Dworkin, The Oregonian, July 21, 2009, at www.oregonlive.com/news/index.ssf/2009/07/more_than_20000_oregonians_urg. html.

122 "Vaccines for Children: Investment in Immunizations Yields Big Dividends," Children Immunizations, National Conference of State Legislatures, 2009, at www.ecom.ncsl.org/programs/health/immuni2.htm.

123 "Childhood Vaccines: Challenges in Preventing Future Shortages," by Janet Heinrich, Subcommittee on Public Health, Committee on Health, Education, Labor, and Pensions, United States Senate and the General Accounting Office, 2002.

amount of lab time, research effort, and financial investment devoted to the search for new vaccines.

The government's over-involvement in the vaccine delivery system has led to price fixing, diminished doctor interest and participation, lowered parental awareness, and fewer children being protected against serious illness. Practical ways to solve these problems include:

1. Focus public health spending on providing vaccinations to children from low-income families, as originally intended by the VFC program.
2. Limit the vaccine purchases of the federal government only to the amount needed to cover children vaccinated through the VFC.
3. Allow doctors to charge fees that cover the true cost of administering vaccines to children.

Currently there is no correlation between the amount the government spends on vaccines and the number of children vaccinated in any given state. It is clear that cost is not the determining factor in achieving high vaccination rates, and that government funding and control does not lead to the universal vaccination of children.

This decline has four consequences. First, it severely restricts competition in the marketplace. Second, it restricts flexibility of supply when demand increases. Third, it limits innovation and research into new vaccines. Fourth, it reduces manufacturers' interest in promoting public health by encouraging the vaccination of children. Hence, the government remains the only organization interested in advertizing and disseminating information on the importance of vaccination, putting immunization of children in direct conflict with other budget and political priorities.

The gap between the amount of government spending on vaccines and the number of children actually vaccinated is a good example of how expected improvements in public health often fail to materialize when government attempts to centrally control people's access to health care.

A better solution would be to target government spending to children of low-income families and to allow doctors, private insurers, and vaccine manufacturers to negotiate rational prices and reasonable reimbursements rates based on voluntary agreement. This would encourage a normal free market to develop, would align the incentives of doctors, parents, and manufacturers for mutual benefit and would serve the public interest by encouraging vaccination for the maximum number of children.

CHAPTER 16

# Certificate of Need Laws

Medical Certificate of Need (CON) laws have existed since the mid-1960s. They are a classic example of government intervention and central planning of the health care delivery system. Their stated purpose is to hold down costs and at the same time provide more charity care. They operate by requiring doctors, hospitals, and clinics to receive government permission before providing more health care services in a given region. Thirty-six states have CON laws.

New York State passed the first CON law in 1966. Businesses, insurers, consumers, and providers came together to study the need for additional hospital beds. The group determined there was a surplus of beds and recommended state officials restrict further hospital expansion with special legislation.[124] The law made it illegal to add beds to an existing hospital or to treat patients in a new facility without first gaining permission from state officials.

The federal government became involved in 1972 when Congress amended the Social Security Act to require all states to review new health care construction projects that exceeded $100,000 in value. Failure to comply with this rule would result in the federal government withholding Medicare and Medicaid money from the offending state.

In 1974, because of exploding costs in health care, Congress passed the National Health Planning and Resource Development Act (NHPRDA). This law established a comprehensive federal health care CON regulation, with the penalty for a state's non-

---

124 "Certificate of Need: State health laws and programs," National Conference of State Legislatures, September, 2015 at http://www.ncsl.org/research/health/concertifi-cate-of-need-state-laws.aspx.

compliance being forfeiture of federal Medicare and Medicaid dollars.[125]

The policy goals of NHPRDA were twofold: to limit the number of health care facilities available to patients in a specific geographic area and, because of more volume and higher payments directed to existing facilities, provide more charity care at those hospitals and clinics allowed to operate in an exclusive area.

States were encouraged to establish their own Certificate of Need programs, and all 50 states complied.

By 1982, however, the federal government realized the national CON law was not saving money but was restricting care and limiting available health services for patients. No increase in charity care occurred. Recognizing this failure, Congress repealed the federal law in 1987, and, subsequently, 14 states repealed their individual CON laws.[126]

The argument in support of the Certificate of Need concept was that the federal government, through Medicare and Medicaid, has paid for health care in the U.S., and this funding, in turn, gave the government the justification to limit the expansion of the health care system through CON laws. The CON restrictions, however, artificially create monopolies and decrease access to health care for patients, leading to Congress's repeal of the national CON law in 1987.

Even though a Certificate of Need law restricts access for patients, many states still have these laws in force. Over 60 percent of all Americans do not have government-paid health insurance, yet these state-based CON laws have an adverse effect on everyone.

The evidence is now clear that CON laws increase the cost of health care. Researchers Stratmann and Russ at George Mason

---

125 National Health Planning and Resources Development Act (NHPRDA) of 1974, Section 2(a)(1), see Public Law 93-641.

126 "Certificate of Need: State health laws and programs," National Conference of State Legislatures, September, 2015 at http://www.ncsl.org/research/health/con-certificate-of-need-state-laws.aspx.

University found that lack of normal competition raised the price of medical care and reduced the availability of hospital beds and medical equipment.[127] An earlier study found an almost 14 percent increase in per-patient health care costs in states with CON laws.[128] The Kaiser Family Foundation reported that health care costs are 11 percent higher overall in states with CON laws compared to states without the restrictive law.[129]

Over the decades, at both the federal and state levels, there has been no evidence that CON laws increase the availability of charity care.[130]

As more patients use high-deductible health insurance plans, and thereby use more of their own money, they should have more choices and better access to health care. Expanded access, increased price competition, and greater medical choice would serve the public interest by allowing new health care services to be provided in communities where they are needed most. For these reasons, the bureaucratically restrictive and long-outdated CON laws should be repealed.

127 "Do certificate of need laws increase indigent care?," by T. Stratmann and J. Russ, Mercatus Center, George Mason University, July, 2014 at http://mercatus.org/sites/default/files/StratmannCertificate-Need.pdf.

128 "Endogenous hospital regulation and its effects on hospital and non-hospital expenditures," by J. Lanning, et. al., Journal of Regulatory Economics, June, 1991 at http://link.springer.com/ article/10.1007%2FBF00140955.

129 "Health care expenditures per capita by state of residence," The Henry J. Kaiser Family Foundation, 2009 at http://kff.org/other/state-indicator/health-spending-per-capita/.

130 "Do certificate of need laws increase indigent care?," by T. Stratmann and J. Russ, Mercatus Center, George Mason University, July, 2014 at http://mercatus.org/sites/default/files/StratmannCertificate-Need.pdf.

# CHAPTER 17

# Examining Proposed Single-payer Systems

As the debate over health care reform rages on, more Americans are considering adoption of a single-payer health care system. The Affordable Care Act (ACA) is a highly complex law and has made our current health care delivery system more confusing.[131] A single-payer system is attractive to many people because of its perceived simplicity—the U.S. government would provide direct health services to all Americans.

To begin with, there is a great degree of confusion concerning the terminology used to describe various health care delivery systems. "Single-payer" health care is a system in which residents are required to pay the government through taxes—in amounts determined by the government—to cover health care costs, rather than purchasing health insurance from private companies in a voluntary and competitive marketplace.[132]

Doctors and other providers in a single-payer system may or may not be government employees. The most recent term for a single-payer system in the United States is "Medicare for All," under which doctors, clinics, and hospitals would be private, but the government would be the sole price-setter and bill-payer.

"Socialized medicine" is a term usually reserved for health care systems that are paid for by taxes and that employ all doctors and

---

131 "The impact of national health care reform on Washington State," by Roger Stark, MD, Policy Brief, Washington Policy Center, January 1, 2010, at http://www.washingtonpolicy. org/publications/detail/ the-impact-of-national-health-care-reform-on-washington-state

132 "Single-payer health care," definition, Wikipedia, at https://en.wikipedia.org/wiki/ Single-payer_ healthcare.

providers as government workers.[133] The Veterans Administration system in the U.S. is a typical example, in which the hospitals and clinics are owned by the government and the doctors and nurses are all government employees.

"Universal" health care refers to a national system in which every citizen is mandated to have health insurance paid for through some combination of private funds and taxes.[134] The insurance may be administered by the government or by private companies with complete oversight by the government. Having "universal" insurance coverage, however, does not guarantee a person actual access to timely health care service.

Virtually every industrialized country has a universal system. Only Canada, and to a certain extent Taiwan, have pure single-payer health care.

Citizens and elected officials in the U.S. have debated the merits of various universal health care proposals for over 100 years. President Franklin Roosevelt pushed for government-run health care under his New Deal initiative. Because of voter mistrust, Roosevelt removed medical services from his proposal, but he retained the Social Security retirement system as an important foundation for his expansion of government.

Thirty years later, President Johnson and Congress passed the Medicare and Medicaid entitlement programs. Medicare is essentially a single-payer system for seniors. Except for federal employees, people 65 years of age and older now have no other choice for major medical health insurance. Medicaid is a pure welfare entitlement for low-income people, paid for by state and federal taxpayers.

The ACA further entrenched government into the U.S. health

---

133 "Socialized medicine," definition, Wikipedia, at https://en.wikipedia.org/wiki/Socialized_medicine.

134 "Universal health care," definition, Wikipedia, at https://en.wikipedia.org/wiki/Universal_health_care.

care system by expanding the Medicaid entitlement and by providing taxpayer subsidies to help individuals purchase health insurance in government-mandated exchanges.[135]

Although the ACA did not deliver "health care for all" as advocates promised and only insures an additional 20 million people (about six percent of the U.S. population), its mandates and regulations affect all areas of the U.S. health care system. It has driven health care costs up, has fragmented health care delivery, and has put the country's health care system in jeopardy.

Consequently, many advocates say the ACA did not go far enough. Americans are now debating whether the government should take over and control all aspects of our health care with a single-payer system.

Senator Bernie Sanders (I-VT) has long advocated for the creation of a single-payer health care system in the United States. His "Medicare for All" is a very robust and specific plan.[136]

The non-partisan Committee for a Responsible Federal Budget (CRFB) analyzed Senator Sanders' original proposal from a financial standpoint.[137] He calls for six new or expanded taxes. Everyone would pay 6.2 percent more in payroll tax and 2.2 percent more in income tax. This combined 8.4 percent tax increase would have the greatest impact on low-income workers, according to the analysis. Rather than receiving "free" Medicaid, these workers would have 8.4 percent less in take-home pay.

High-income workers would experience four additional taxes. Income taxes would increase, capital gains would be taxed as ordinary income, certain current deductions would be eliminated,

135 The patient-centered solution; our health care crisis, how it happened, and how we can fix it, by Roger Stark, MD, 2012.

136 "Medicare for all: leaving no one behind," Bernie Sanders Campaign Website, 2016, at https://berniesanders.com/ issues/medicare-for-all/.

137 "Analysis of the Sanders single-payer offsets," Committee for Responsible Federal Budget, February 3, 2016, at http:// www.crfb.org/blogs/analysis-sanders-single-payer-offsets.

and estate taxes would increase. Marginal tax rates for people earning between $18,550 and $75,300 would go from 30.3 percent to 38.9 percent. For higher-income workers (those with incomes greater than $250,000), income plus payroll taxes would go up to 77 percent, and capital gains taxes would reach 64 percent.

Even with these expanded taxes, the CRFB reports that multiple analysts, including the non-partisan Congressional Budget Office, find Senator Sanders' calculations to be short of the funding needed by $14 trillion to $32 trillion over ten years. Although the tax increase would be staggering, the overall impact on the U.S. economy and economic growth would be devastating. There are now several examples of countries that enacted socialist programs and ultimately became mired in stagnant economies.

The Medicare program, created in 1965, was nine times over the original budget estimate by 1990. There is no reason to believe a huge government entitlement like "Medicare for All" would remain under its proposed budget.

Half of all Americans receive their health insurance from their employer or their spouse's employer. "Medicare for All" would eliminate employer-paid health insurance and force all of these workers into the government-run, single-payer plan.

Vermont came close to instituting a single-payer system on a state-level basis. In 2011, the legislature passed, and Governor Pete Shumlin signed "An Act Relating to a Universal and Unified Health System." The state-wide, single-payer system was to start in 2017. By 2014, however, fiscal estimates showed that the state budget would need an extra $2 billion in 2017 to fund the program. This would be a 35 percent increase over the state's original $5.7 billion 2017 budget.[138] The state would need to raise taxes to levels unacceptable to the public, and at the same time, decrease provider payments

---

138 "2017 Fiscal facts, Vermont Legislature, Joint Fiscal Office," at http://www.leg.state. vt.us/jfo/publications/2017%20 Fiscal%20Facts%20--%20Final.pdf.

to unrealistic amounts. Vermont officials admitted failure and abandoned the plan in December 2014.[139]

A recurring argument in favor of a single-payer system is that U.S. health care ranks poorly when compared to other countries. The most commonly quoted publication that ranks countries' health care delivery system is a World Health Organization (WHO) study from 2000.[140] The U.S. ranked the out of 191 countries in the report, behind Greece, Morocco, and Columbia.

The paper's authors placed a ranking-number on five separate health care delivery system criteria and then added the results of those five to get a total number for each country. From the paper itself:

" ...country attainment on all five indicators (i.e., health, health inequality, responsiveness-level, responsiveness-distribution, and fair-financing) were rescaled...Then the following weights were used to construct the overall composite measure: 25% for health, 25% for health inequality, 12.5% for the level of responsiveness, 12.5% for the distribution of responsiveness, and 25% for fairness in financing. These weights are based on a survey carried out by WHO to elicit stated preferences of individuals in their relative valuations of the goals of the health system."

The WHO-selected criteria of health inequality, distribution of responsiveness, and fairness in financing give an advantage to countries with either a single-payer system or countries with some form of universal health insurance coverage. In other words, because the U.S. does not have a top-down, government-run health care system, America began the rankings with a 62.5 percent handicap. We ranked very well in the health and level of responsiveness categories.

---

139 "Six reasons why Vermont's single-payer health plan was doomed from the start," by Avik Roy, Forbes Online, December 21, 2014, at https://www.forbes.com/sites/theapothecary/2014/12/21/6-reasons-why-vermonts-single-payerhealth-plan-was-doomed-from-the-start/#7111b7fd4850

140 "Measuring Overall Health System Performance For 191 Countries," by A. Tandon, C. Murray, J. Lauer, and D. Evans, World Health Organization, 2000, at https://www.who.int/healthinfo/paper30.pdf.

The tragedy is that the ranking of thirty-seventh is used repeatedly in health care debates and does a disservice to the excellent medical outcomes and overall responsiveness of the current U.S. health care system. The high quality of the U.S. system is indicated by the strong desire of many sick people from around the world to travel to the United States for treatment.

In another flawed publication, the Commonwealth Fund has serially tracked the health care delivery systems of 11 first-world counties. The U.S. has ranked last in all of the Fund's reports for the past 15 years.[141] As with the WHO study, the U.S. is severely penalized in the rankings for not having some form of socialized universal health coverage.

The Fund's studies also rank the U.S. poorly for medical outcomes, specifically infant mortality, longevity after age 60, and preventable mortality. However, there are explanations for these results.

The U.S. records every birth, whereas many other countries record a "live" birth only if the infant has survived a certain number of days or weeks. Longevity after 60 in the U.S. varies by only one to two years compared with other countries. And finally, preventable mortality reflects patients that actually sought medical help. If a patient died at home or of "natural causes," this is not reflected in the overall results.

Again, for treatment of specific disease entities, such as heart failure, diabetes, and many forms of cancer, the U.S. results are enviable by world standards.

To control costs, increase choice, and maintain and improve quality, patients must be allowed to control their own health care dollars and make their own health care decisions. A single-payer system would move policy in the other direction. It would further

---

141 "Mirror, Mirror on the Wall, 2014 Update: How the U.S. Health Care System Compares Internationally," by K. Davis, K. Stremikis, D. Squires, and C. Schoen, the Commonwealth Fund, June 16, 2014, at https://www.commonwealthfund.org/publications/fund-reports/2014/jun/mirror-mirror-wall-2014-update-how-us-health-care-system.

entrench the inefficient and costly government management of health care delivery for Americans.

No government bureaucrat is more concerned about a person's health than that person is. Patients, as health care consumers, should be allowed to be informed about, to review the prices of, and to gain access to the best health care services available in a fair, open, and free marketplace. As the real-world examples of Canada and Vermont show, a single-payer system does none of these things.

CHAPTER 18

# Health Care
# in Other Countries

The U.S. is now at a health care crossroads. Progressives on the left are strongly arguing for greater public-sector control through a single-payer, government-run system or through incremental moves toward such a system. A Medicare or Medicaid buy-in, dropping the age of Medicare eligibility, and a public option are gaining traction in the national debate. The private alternative revolves around more consumerism, with measures that give patients more direct control over their health care dollars and medical decisions.

Other countries' health care systems are frequently cited as providing the solution for the U.S. It is not clear, however, whether systems in other countries offer a workable health care model for Americans.

## Canada

The Canadian federal government passed the Canadian Health Care Act (CHA) in 1984. It is a pure single-payer system. Every Canadian is covered by the plan and theoretically has access to medical care. The provinces administer the plan with funding from federal taxpayers. The government determines what procedures are medically necessary based on data and statistics.[142]

The CHA is a pay-as-you-go plan, which depends on having enough younger workers to pay for the health care of older and sicker individuals. Seventy-five percent of Canadians have supplementary insurance for items such as drugs and eye-glasses that the CHA does not cover.

---

142 "Canada's health care system," Government of Canada, at https://www.canada.ca/en/health-canada/services/canadahealth-care-system.html.

The supply of health care is overwhelmed by the demand in Canada, leading to severe shortages. Consequently, medical care is rationed through the use of long waiting lists and through limits placed on the number of certain medical procedures. Wait times vary by province and medical specialty, but on average, 29 percent of adults who became ill waited two months or more to see a doctor, and 18 percent waited four months or more in 2016. Specialty care in Canada is even harder to access. In 1993, the median wait time in ten provinces across 12 medical specialties was 9.3 weeks. By 2018, the wait had increased to 20 weeks.[143]

Long wait times are more than an inconvenience for Canadians. Simple medical problems, if not treated early, can turn into chronic or life-threatening conditions. Wait times at the very least prolong pain, mental stress, and suffering for patients.[144]

In Canada, health care costs have skyrocketed and now represent the largest expense for every province's budget. Ontario, for example, spent 43 percent of its budget on health care in 2010. Estimates show that Ontario will spend 80 percent of its budget on health care in 2030.[145]

Almost 90 percent of Canadians live within driving distance of the United States. For those Canadians who can afford it and do not want to wait, quality health care is available in the U.S. without waiting. In reality, Canada has a two-tiered health care system, with the U.S. providing timely care for those willing and able to travel and pay more.

---

143 Waiting your turn; wait times for health care in Canada, 2018 report," by Bacchus Barua and Feixue Ren, Fraser Institute, November 2018, at https://www.fraserinstitute.org/sites/default/files/waiting-your-turn-wait-times-forhealth-care-in-canada-2018.pdf.

144 "If universal health care is the goal, don't copy Canada," by Jason Clemens and Bacchus Barua, Forbes Online, June 13, 2014, at https://www.forbes.com/sites/theapothecary/2014/06/13/if-universal-health-care-is-the-goal-dont-copycanada/#3a833ec678d5.

145 "The sustainability of health care spending in Canada 2017," by B. Barua, M. Palacios, and J. Emes, Fraser Institute, March 2017, at https://www.fraserinstitute.org/sites/default/files/sustainability-of-health-care-spending-incanada-2017.pdf 4.

## Great Britain

Great Britain established a comprehensive government health care system in 1948. The National Health Service (NHS) essentially gives every citizen cradle-to-grave coverage. The national system provides open access to primary care, although the general practitioner may not be of the patient's choosing. There are very modest copays and basically no hospital charges. The entitlement is financed through general taxes as well as a small payroll tax on workers. About ten percent of the population has private insurance, and many physicians combine government entitlement work with private practice.

Health services are planned and approved by regional government agencies called Clinical Commissioning Groups. These commissions determine the value of specific treatments, who can receive them, and the number of these procedures that the NHS will provide in any given area of the country.[146]

Like many nationalized health care systems, it is difficult for people in need of care to turn their theoretical legal entitlement into access to actual health care service. Most rationing under these systems takes the form of long waiting lists. Wait times for diagnostic and specialty care in Britain became so long that the government ruled in 2010 no one should have to wait more than 18 weeks (four-and-a-half months) for treatment.[147]

Over the past year, 250,000 citizens have waited more than six months for planned treatments within the NHS, while 36,000 British have waited nine months or more.[148] Twenty-five percent of

---

146 "BrItain's Version of 'Medicare For All' Is Struggling With Long Waits For Care," by S. Pipes, Forbes.com, April 1, 2019, at https://www.forbes.com/sites/sallypipes/2019/04/01/britains-version-of-medicare-for-all-is-collapsing/#27c4b71436b8.

147 "Happy birthday to Great Britain's increasingly scandalous National Health Service," by Scott Atlas, MD, Forbes.com, July 5, 2013, at http://www.forbes.com/sites/scottatlas/2013/07/05/happy-birthday-to-great-britains-increasingly-scandalousnation-al-health-service/.

148 "BrItain's Version of 'Medicare For All' Is Struggling With Long Waits For Care," by S. Pipes, Forbes.com, April 1, 2019, at https://www.forbes.com/sites/sallypipes/2019/04/01/britains-version-of-medicare-for-all-is-collapsing/#27c4b71436b8.

cancer patients did not start their treatment at the recommended time. This is reflected in poor survival times for the common cancers of breast and prostate.

Wait times are less in the private sector and offer an alternative for those patients with the financial resources to seek private care.

Medical and administrative inefficiencies are rampant, and chronic shortages, with resulting rationing, are commonplace. Some British families have filed lawsuits claiming medical neglect of elderly parents or grandparents who died waiting to receive care. Heavy workloads are causing older doctors to retire early. The country faces a shortage of both physicians and nurses.

In spite of these problems, most British citizens have a positive, if not enthusiastic, opinion of their health care delivery system, seeing it as a source of national pride.

## Germany

Germany was the first country to institute a comprehensive form of socialized health care, starting in 1883. Today, health insurance is mandatory for all German citizens and is financed through employer and employee contributions as well as the general tax fund.[149] Because of ever-increasing costs, the contribution from the general tax fund is increasing. Accident and long-term care insurance are separate but are part of the overall health care delivery system.

Anyone earning less than $71,000 a year is automatically placed in one of 118 government insurance or "sickness" funds. Eighty-five percent of all Germans are enrolled in the government plans. People who earn more than $71,000 can choose to enroll in one of 42 private insurance funds, although 75 percent of these higher-income individuals have chosen to remain in the government plans.

Private insurance plans pay providers more than the government

---

149 "The German Health Care System," by M. Blumel and R. Busse, International Health Care Systems Profile, The Commonwealth Fund, 2016, at https://international.commonwealthfund.org/countries/germany/.

funds, and, consequently, doctors will give private patients priority.[150] Deductibles can vary, but all funds are tightly controlled by agencies composed of government officials and providers.

Although 84 percent of Germans say they are satisfied with their health care system, there is a growing egalitarian movement to eliminate the private insurance funds and place everyone in a single, socialized government plan.

### Switzerland

Switzerland has had mandated health insurance since 1996. The country uses a model of government "managed competition" with an individual mandate to purchase health insurance. It is not employer-based and relies on "private" insurers who must honor guaranteed issue rules (they must sell to anyone regardless of pre-existing conditions) and community rating (all people except for smokers are placed in the same risk pool).[151] All hospitals are private but heavily regulated by the government.

Individuals pay approximately 30 percent of their health care expenses out of pocket, and the government subsidizes nearly one-third of the cost of covering all Swiss citizens.

Insurance companies set payments to doctors in a cartel fashion and compete on policy price and benefits. Basic benefit packages are determined by the government. Because of organized special interests, the political influence of the government is constantly expanding the mandatory basic benefit package, putting upward pressure on insurance prices.

Because employers are not involved and because the Swiss pay a

---

150 "Why Germans Love Their Health Insurance," by S. Kimball, Handelsbatt Today, May 15, 2017, at https://www.handelsblatt.com/today/politics/handelsblatt-explains-why-germans-love-their-health-insurance/23569646.html?ticket=ST-1005727-3KxYSepLAcxY-Jgml7M1k-ap6.

151 "Health care reform: lowering costs by putting patients in charge," by R. Stark, MD, Policy Brief, Washington Policy Center, June, 2015, at https://www.washingtonpolicy.org/library/docLib/Stark- Health care reform and alternatives to the Affordable Care Act.pdf.

high percent out of pocket, patients are well informed about the full cost of their health care. This has led to a greater degree of informed consumerism in health care than exists in other countries.

Eighty-one percent of Swiss citizens say they have a "positive" impression of their health care system.[152] Wait times are not a problem, yet because the list of government-mandated benefits in any insurance plan continues to grow, the Swiss are paying more and finding fewer options for health insurance.

### Japan

Japan socialized its health delivery system in 1961, when the country required everyone to join a health insurance plan directed by the government. The entire system is essentially a pay-as-you-go plan. Retirees, the self-employed, and the unemployed are covered by the National Health Insurance Plan (NHIP), and workers are enrolled in one of the various employee plans. The NHIP is funded by the government, and the employee plans are equally funded by employers and workers. Monthly premiums differ based on salary.

Waiting to receive health care services is not currently a problem, but overutilization is rampant, leading to exploding costs.[153] Since 1995, when extrapolation of spending trends revealed that by year 2025 Japan would be consuming 50 percent of its GDP for medical care, the Japanese system has undergone gradual reform. Seniors must now pay an increasing fixed premium, and worker copays have gone from ten percent to 20 percent. Likewise, physician reimbursement has been adjusted downward and continues to be reevaluated.

---

152 "Swiss are happy with their health – more or less," by J. Wurz, Health Monitor 2016, swissinfo.ch, June 24, 2016, at https://www.swissinfo.ch/eng/health-monitor-2016_swiss-are-happy-with-their-health-more-or-less/42249778.

153 "Japan's buckling health care system at a crossroads," by T. Otake, The Japan Times, February 19, 2017, at https://www.japantimes.co.jp/news/2017/02/19/national/japans-buckling-health-care-system-crossroads/#.XQl_W4hKjIV.

## France

France's current health care system began in 1945, and "statutory" health insurance, as defined in law, is compulsory. Funding is through a combination of employer and employee payroll tax (50 percent), mandatory and dedicated income tax (35 percent), and taxes on drug manufacturers, alcohol, and tobacco (15 percent). Private insurance covers only deductibles and some copays.[154]

Available treatments, pricing, and copays are determined by the government. Doctors may be government employees or may be in private practice. Sixty-five percent of hospitals are government-run, 25 percent are private for-profit, and the remainder are private not-for-profit (most of these are cancer facilities).

Wait times vary by patient location and doctor specialty but can run from six to eighty days.[155] For example, the wait to see a dentist averages four weeks, a gynecologist six weeks, a cardiologist seven weeks, and a dermatologist eleven weeks. When the French believe the wait is too long, over half will seek another doctor, and a third will forgo being seen at all by a provider. The French attribute the long wait times to a lack of physicians.

France is struggling with increasing costs, a doctor shortage, and an aging demographic.[156] The response of elected officials to these problems is to impose more government regulation and control.

## Singapore

Singapore is a city-state made up of 5.8 million people. It is a relatively new country, having established sovereignty in 1965. It has

---

154 "The French Health Care System," by I. Durand-Zaleski, International Health Care System Profiles, The Commonwealth Fund, 2016, at https://international.commonwealth-fund.org/countries/france/.

155 What are the average waiting times to see doctors in France?," by B. McPartland, The Local, October 19, 2018, at https://www.thelocal.fr/20181009/what-are-the-average-wait-ing-times-to-see-doctors-in-france.

156 "Macron announces changes to France's health care system," by S. Corbet, Medicalxpress, September 18, 2018, at https://medicalxpress.com/news/2018-09-macron-france-health.html.

a booming economy and ranks as one of the most expensive cities in which to live.

Its health care system is truly two tiered, with 30 percent of spending occurring in the public sector and 70 percent in the private sector. Both private and public sectors are heavily controlled by the government, and health insurance is mandatory.[157] Hospitals offer five levels of care, where the most expensive rooms are single-patient with air conditioning, private doctors, and other amenities. The least expensive level places patients in wards with seven or eight other patients who are all treated by government-employed physicians.

The government mandates that all workers set up three savings accounts; one for housing, education, and investments, one for retirement, and one for health care spending (this account functions like a health savings account).

The government also offers a second, non-mandated insurance plan for catastrophic medical problems. The cost of this insurance is very inexpensive, and most citizens have it. It kicks in after the deductibles and copays paid by the patient are exhausted.

A third program is a safety-net plan that begins when the patient has exhausted his or her health savings account. The amount of financial support given to a patient depends on income, social situation, and is decided at a very local level.

### Sweden

Sweden has a universal health care system that is overseen by the federal government but administered on a local level by county councils.[158] Health care in Sweden began as a socialized system in the

---

157 "What Makes Singapore's Health Care So Cheap?," by A. Carroll and A. Frakt, The New York Times, October 2, 2017, at https://www.nytimes.com/2017/10/02/upshot/what-makes-singapores-health-care-so-cheap.html.

158 "Facts about Sweden's health care system," Swedish Health Care Academy, at https://www.swedishhealthcare.se/about-sweden-and-swedish-healthcare/swedens-healthcare-system/.

eighteenth century, but the specific administration through county councils began in 1928.[159] Local taxes pay for 70 percent of costs, and the national government pays for 20 percent. Private insurance accounts for less than one percent of overall costs, and patients cover the balance of health care expenses. The government controls costs through a budget ceiling and through a national committee that "promotes the efficient utilization of (health care) resources."

Doctor office visits and most pharmaceuticals are paid for out of pocket. The federal government sets ceilings for these charges. Children and adolescences receive free care. The overriding goals of Sweden's health care system are "equal access," "care based on need," and "cost effectiveness." The government determines the effectiveness of various treatments and "some" expensive treatments are covered. The government has the ability to deny treatment if officials determine a particular level of patient care is unjustified.

Most doctors are employed by the county councils, which also manage the majority of hospitals. Private hospitals exist, although they contract with the local county council.

Swedish law states that no patient can wait longer than 90 days, although the law has little real meaning since 30 percent of patients wait longer. In addition to long wait times, many parts of the country face a doctor and nurse shortage.[160] As the population ages, wait times are becoming longer, and the number of citizens frustrated by the shortcomings of the system grows.

## Italy

Officials in Italy nationalized their health care delivery system in the 1970s. Every citizen has health insurance through the government,

---

159 "Health care systems in transition," World Health Organization, 1996, at http://www. euro.who.int/_data/assets/pdf_file/0016/120283/E72481.pdf.

160 "Swedes enjoy world class health care – when they can get it," by G. Hodan, Medical press, September 3, 2018, at https://medicalxpress.com/news/2018-09-swedes-world-class-healthcarewhen.html.

although private insurance and doctors are available, mainly in the larger cities such as Milan and Rome.[161]

The system is financed by local and national taxes, and treatments are free at the point of service.[162] There are small out-of-pocket expenses for pharmaceuticals and modest copays for some doctor visits. The largest problem facing Italian officials is financial—staying within budgets.

The majority of Italians are not pleased with their health care system. On a scale of one (worst) to ten (best), Italians rate the socialized system at 3.7 and the competency of their government-paid doctors at 4.6.[163] There is a wide divergence of medical outcomes and overall satisfaction with Italian health care. Citizens in the wealthy north of Italy seem to do much better than those living in regions in the impoverished south.

Looking to other countries to solve our health care delivery system problems may not be reasonable. Other countries are smaller than the U.S. and have a more homogenous population. What the people of one country favor may not be applicable or acceptable to people living in a different society.

One fact does remain, though. In all other countries examined, the demand for health care far outstrips the money budgeted for it. The results of this supply/demand mismatch are chronic shortages followed by strict rationing of health care. The rationing can take many forms—from long waits, to denying the elderly access to certain procedures, to allowing individuals with political influence to "jump the que" and receive priority attention from providers.

---

161 "Health Care in Italy," International Living, at https://internationalliving.com/countries/italy/health-care-in-italy/.

162 "Italy: health system review," by F. Ferre, et. al., NCBI, PubMed, 2014, at https://www.ncbi.nlm.nih.gov/pubmed/25471543.

163 "Italians are Unhappy with Health Care in Italy," by A. Roe, Italy Chronicles, October 9, 2012, at http://www.italychronicles.com/italians-unhappy-healthcare-italy/.

The United States spends 18 percent of its annual economy on health care. Other industrialized countries spend between eight and eleven percent of their GDP on health care. Yet each of these countries is experiencing greater demand and rising costs.

Just as in the U.S., every other country faces the demographic problem of an aging population and a relatively decreasing work force to pay taxes for their seniors' health care. This age mis-match is creating health care budget problems for most other countries.

Further, the legal system in other countries is not as active or contentious as it is in the United States. Lawsuits contribute a higher percent of overall health care costs in the U.S. than in other countries.[164] Hospitals and doctors in the U.S. pay much higher malpractice insurance rates and are more vulnerable to lawsuits than in other cultures. In addition, the practice of "defensive medicine," ordering unneeded tests and procedures to guard against litigation, adds to costs in the U.S.

Canada has a true single-payer, nationalized system that is totally funded by taxpayers. In reality, it is a two-tiered system in the sense that Canadian officials allow their citizens to travel to the U.S. for privately funded health care. All other industrialized countries have mandated universal health insurance coverage but allow some form of a private sector to compete with government plans. These are not truly free-market systems because the government retains firm control of the practice of medicine in the private sectors.

While there is no question that the U.S. spends more on health care than other industrialized countries, the U.S. also leads the world in financing medical innovations. We pay three times as much for drugs as patients in other countries, where government officials

---

164 "The cost of medical malpractice lawsuits in Washington state – Lessons from Texas reform," by R. Stark, MD, Policy Note, Washington Policy Center, April, 2016, at https://www.washingtonpolicy.org/library/doclib/Stark-Update-on-the-cost-of-medical-malpractice-lawsuits-in-Washington-State-Lessons-from-Texas-reform.pdf.

have negotiated prices with pharmaceutical companies.[165] The U.S. also leads the world in medical and biologic research, which is the foundation for the development of innovative medical devices.[166]

By paying higher prices, the reality is that patients in the U.S. finance the research and development of new life-saving and life-extending drugs and medical devices for the rest of the world. The health care budgets in other countries are dedicated almost exclusively to patient care rather than research, and these socialized systems rely on medical innovations and drugs developed in the U.S.

Is there some combination of measures from other countries that the U.S. can utilize in reforming our health care delivery system? Although the overall systems vary, the common factor for all other countries is government-mandated health insurance. Even those countries that have a component of "private" health care continue to mandate that every citizen have health insurance.

While universal health insurance coverage is a worthy goal, the critical point is utilizing the best mechanism to allow the greatest number of Americans access to health care. The Canadian single-payer system does not guarantee timely access. The American experience with the Veterans Administration hospital system, a comprehensive government-controlled, single-payer health care program, reveals unacceptable wait times and huge inefficiencies. Fundamentally, these systems ration health care by waiting lists and limited money. The quality of care veterans receive is variable.

Congress tried to force universal health insurance on all Americans through the Affordable Care Act. This was doomed to fail, however, because the same law required all insurance plans to contain

---

165 "The global burden of medical innovation," by D. Goldman and D. Lakdawalla, Brookings Institution, January 30, 2018, at https://www.brookings.edu/research/the-global-burden-of-medical-innovation/.

166 "The Most Innovative Countries in Biology and Medicine," by M. Herper, forbes. com, March 23, 2011, at https://www.forbes.com/sites/matthewherper/2011/03/23/the-most-innovative-countries-in-biology-and-medicine/#1dfeaedb1a71.

expensive and unwanted benefit mandates. The law compounded this insurance regulation problem by forcing companies to sell health insurance to people after they had become ill. Young and healthy individuals have made a reasonable economic decision and have opted to not buy health insurance that they don't want and can't use.

Switzerland has a comparatively large private health care sector, and patients are responsible for 30 percent of their own health care costs. Consequently, a certain degree of health care consumerism exists in Switzerland, and the country has been fairly successful in holding down costs. Unfortunately, as officials increase the number of benefit mandates required in insurance plans, health care costs are rising.

Singapore has a multi-tiered system with different levels of care depending on the patient's ability and willingness to pay more. This is similar to the system in the U.S. before the passage of Medicare and Medicaid, when private hospitals and doctors treated paying patients, and charity hospitals and residents-in-training cared for indigent patients.

The United States is a melting-pot of diverse cultures with a strong tradition of respecting freedom of choice. While smaller countries with a more homogenous population can require that everyone must have health insurance, the majority of Americans object to such a government mandate. Health care system reform must address and comply with the uniqueness of the American culture.

CHAPTER 19

# Patient-oriented
# Health Care Reform

The Affordable Care Act was designed to slow rapidly rising health care costs and to provide affordable health insurance to every legal resident in the United States. Although the law has never enjoyed popular support, polls show that the majority of Americans want the law reformed and improved rather than repealed.[167]

The ACA contains certain provisions that people find attractive, such as requiring insurance companies to sell health insurance to anyone regardless of pre-existing medical conditions. The law has been altered, but politically, total repeal appears unlikely.[168]

From a practical standpoint, would reforming the ACA be significant enough in light of the other government programs (Medicare and Medicaid) and employer spending on health care? Would changes to the ACA be enough to improve the health care financial crisis and expand affordable insurance coverage to all citizens?

Health care spending was fairly constant, between three and five percent of GDP, from 1930 to 1965. Health care costs exploded after the passage of Medicare and Medicaid in 1965. The vast majority of federal spending on health care now is caused by these two programs.

The increasing cost of the ACA is certainly adding to the burden of public spending, but even future ACA spending increases will

167 "Which is more unpopular: Obamacare or repealing Obamacare," by Steve Cantorno, Politifact, April 21, 2014, at http://www.politifact.com/truth-o-meter/statements/2014/apr/21/democratic-national-committee/which-more-unpopular-obamacare-orrepealing-obamac/.

168 "GOP can't give up Obamacare repeal talk," by David Nather, Politico, October 13, 2014, at http://www.politico.com/story/2014/10/gop-cant-give-up-obamacare-repealtalk-111835.html.

make up only a small part of overall government spending on health care.

## Policy recommendations to reform and modernize Medicare

A fair and workable solution to the Medicare problem must account for the reasonable expectations of both the older and younger generations, as well as provide reliable health coverage for future generations. As a country, we have a moral obligation to seniors already enrolled in the program and to those approaching retirement age.

A simple first step to Medicare reform would be to gradually raise the age of eligibility. When the program started in 1965, the average life expectancy in the U.S. was 67 years for men and 74 years for women. Average life expectancy is now up to 76 years for men and 81 years for women, straining an entitlement program that was not designed to provide health services to people for so many years late in life.

Another simple Medicare reform would be more thorough means testing, not just in Part B of the program. Under tighter means testing, wealthier seniors would pay more, and low-income people would pay less.

As it stands now, there is, understandably, no private insurance market for seniors. Any private market was crowded out long ago by the tax-funded Medicare. It is virtually impossible for any private company or individual to compete against the government, which has monopoly power and an unlimited ability to fix prices and lose money while any potential competitors go out of business.

The private market for the elderly could be resurrected by allowing people to opt out of Medicare voluntarily and allowing those seniors to purchase health savings accounts and high-deductible health plans. Low-income seniors could use vouchers or some type of subsidized premium support that would allow them to purchase health insurance in the private market.

Physicians should be allowed to seek partial payments from patients or their insurance companies, which, by law, they cannot do now unless they leave the Medicare program entirely.

Future generations should be allowed to continue the individual health insurance they want to keep into retirement. Not surprisingly, younger people as a group are healthier than older people, so as the younger generation saves, their health insurance nest egg would build until they need it in their later years. This is the same strategy that millions of individuals and families use today to prepare for retirement. The federal government informs people that they cannot rely only on Social Security to support them after age 67, and that all working people need to plan for the expected living expenses they will incur later on in life. The same should be true of Medicare regarding future health care costs.

## Policy recommendations to reform and modernize Medicaid

The most important first step to reforming the federal Medicaid program is to redesign it so it no longer functions as an unsustainable, open-ended entitlement. Welfare reform in the late 1990s was successful because it placed limits on how many years people could expect to receive taxpayer support. Medicaid recipients should have a copay requirement based on income and ability to pay.

Where applicable, Medicaid enrollees should have a work requirement. Like welfare, Medicaid should be viewed not as a permanent lifestyle, but as a transition program to help low-income families achieve self-confidence, economic independence, and full self-sufficiency.

It is condescending to believe poor families cannot manage their own health care. Allowing them to control their own health care dollars through subsidized HSAs or premium vouchers would financially reward enrollees for leading a healthy lifestyle and making smart personal choices. It would also show respect for low-income families, allowing them to be treated equally with others in the community.

Local control of the management and financing of entitlement programs works best. States, rather than the federal government, should be placed in charge of administering Medicaid. Block grants and waivers from the federal government would allow states to experiment with program designs that work best for their residents and to budget for Medicaid spending more efficiently.

The income requirement should be returned to 133 percent of the federal poverty level. Medicaid should not be a subsidized "safety net" for middle-income people by encouraging those who can live independently to become dependent for their health care on a tax-subsidized entitlement program.

### Policy recommendations to reform or repeal the ACA

The ACA includes allowing states to set up health insurance exchanges to distribute federal subsidies to help low- and medium-income people pay for mandated health insurance. Exchanges, both the state agencies and the federally-run website, are extremely expensive and have been fraught with technical problems. In many cases, they much less efficiently duplicate consumer services already provided for free by private markets and brokers.

Subsidies, or premium supports, or even tax credits could be given directly to individuals without the need for a cumbersome government exchange. This would streamline the system and give consumers greater choice while still providing people needed financial support.

People already receiving subsidies in the ACA exchanges could gradually transition to the reformed individual insurance market. More competition and more choice in this market would lower premium prices and allow people to purchase plans they truly want.

In addition to reform of the exchanges, the expanded Medicaid as allowed by the ACA should be reformed as discussed above.

## The free market

There is wide agreement that the health care system was dysfunctional before the ACA became law. Going back to the situation as it existed before 2010 is not a solution. The country has two choices at this point: impose more government control or move toward more patient control.

Buying coverage and using health care services is an economic activity. Because of the close relationship between patients and providers, it is the most personal of all economic endeavors. So why are costs increasing and quality being questioned in health care and not other economic areas? For example, food production has grown exponentially with lower costs. The price, choice, and quality of clothing have improved, and the availability of other goods and services broaden every day. Prices for electronic goods and telecommunication devices drop steadily, while quality and performance continually increase.

The basic difference between health care and these other economic activities is the fact that consumers use their own dollars to purchase these other goods and services. Almost 90 percent of health care in the U.S. has historically been purchased for the consumer by a third party.

Some argue that health care is so essential and often needed so quickly that normal consumer choices are not possible. How does a person make an informed choice while experiencing a heart attack or stroke or other major incident? It turns out that almost 90 percent of health care delivery in the U.S. is planned and routine, while only about ten percent is of an emergency nature.[169] For most medical care, the patient has time to become a knowledgeable consumer.

In a free and open insurance market, competitive policies for emergency medical coverage would be chosen by individuals long

---

169 "Here's Why Price Transparency Can Revolutionize Health Care," by T. Coburn, MD, Fox Business at https://www.openthebooks.com/fox-business-tom-coburn-heres-why-price-transparency-can-revolutionize-health-care/.

before an emergency arises. Likewise, community standards for free emergency medical care could be established, just as we have with firefighting, policing, and 911 disaster services.

In a truly free market, the patient as a consumer would benefit immediately from the effects of competition and improving technology. The motivator for cost awareness in health care would be eliminating third-party payers and allowing patients to control their own health care dollars. This would increase competition, increase innovation at lower costs, ensure quality, and improve access. It is arrogant for opponents of consumer empowerment to argue that people cannot become wise consumers of health care.

### Knowing prices of health care

For patients to become informed consumers of health care, they must first know the true price of the services they receive. Doctors and hospitals should publish their prices and compete, not only on quality, but also on retail prices. When people spend their own money, they become smart shoppers. This would be true of health care too.

This shift would be a major change for providers and patients, but in other areas of life, Americans have a long history of consumerism. Through consumer reports, second opinions, the Internet, and other tools, most patients would learn to make wise health care decisions.

### Change the tax code to reduce dependence on employer-provided coverage

Employer-paid health insurance is a firmly established tradition in the U.S. because the tax code rewards employers, but not individuals or families, in buying health insurance. This has caused a huge distortion in health care spending because most employers are ill-suited to make sensitive choices about health coverage for their employees. Everyone wants a healthy workforce, yet employers don't pay for other necessities of a healthy life, such as food, shelter, and clothing.

To allow individuals to control their own health care dollars, the tax code should be changed to let all individuals take the same tax deduction for health insurance costs that employers have had since 1943. A change in mind-set is also needed to eliminate the idea that employers should provide employee health coverage. Employer-paid health insurance is an example of tax policy dictating health care policy.

Similar proposals include federal law providing a level of insurance premium support or earned tax credit. The details of the various proposals differ, but the core concept is based on patients as consumers controlling their own health care dollars.

### Insurance regulatory reform

Policymakers should change how they view health insurance. Instead of government-mandated "insurance" and entitlement programs that attempt to cover every possible health-related activity, health coverage needs to work like other forms of indemnity insurance used to mitigate risk, such as car, homeowners, and life insurance.

Just as it makes little sense to use insurance to pay for gas or to mow the lawn, policymakers need to get away from the idea that health insurance should cover all our health-related events. True indemnity insurance should be there for catastrophes and emergencies. Routine day-to-day health services should be paid for out of pocket as needed.

We have a good policy mechanism to do this today through the use of health savings accounts (HSAs, as discussed below). These accounts require a person or family to purchase a high-deductible catastrophic policy to cover high-dollar medical expenses but allow a tax-advantaged savings account to save for day-to-day medical-related purchases. Savings can be accumulated from year to year, and the balance in an individual's personal account can be taken from one job to another.

## Eliminate costly mandates

Part of insurance reform would be to eliminate provider and benefit mandates imposed by government in insurance plans. Mandates set by government officials and policymakers now restrict patient choice in the purchase of health insurance.

Supporters of mandates say no one can predict a patient's future needs, so the government should require people by law to buy expensive coverage. That is true, but a catastrophic, high-deductible insurance plan can be designed to cover any future major medical problem. Affordable auto and homeowner insurance policies, except in very unusual circumstances, cover any and all major problems and provide individuals and families with thousands of dollars of coverage should the need arise.

Mandates are a classic example of politically powerful interest groups lobbying elected officials to include payment for their services in every insurance policy. Mandates restrict competition, drive up prices, and greatly restrict choices for patients.

A reasonable first step would be to allow the interstate purchase of health insurance. Patients would have a huge increase in their choices, and the market would become much more competitive. The health coverage that some state governments mandate would still be available, but consumers would make their own decisions about whether to buy it.

## Pre-existing conditions and high-risk pools

One of the most popular features of the ACA is the fact that insurance companies cannot deny coverage to a person because of a pre-existing medical condition. The result is higher insurance costs for everyone, as insurance companies seek to make up for their losses by charging higher prices to their healthy policyholders. Instead of forcing everyone to buy insurance (individual mandate) or forcing everyone to pay higher premiums to cover those with pre-existing conditions, a better plan would be to set up voluntary high-risk pools.

These state-run pools would provide health insurance for those people with high medical costs who find insurance on the private market to be too expensive. As noted in Chapter 2, a relatively small percent of all patients use a high percent of health care. High-risk pools would support these patients while allowing the majority of Americans to purchase lower-priced health insurance. Various funding and subsidy mechanisms, such as a small universal premium tax, would be much more efficient and less costly than the current one-size-fits-all system.

## Tort reform

Unlike other western countries, the United States has a very active legal system, and hospitals, doctors, and other health care providers must constantly manage the impending threat of costly medical lawsuits.

Medical outcomes in the U.S. are no worse, and by many measures are much better, than those in other countries. Yet our legal system artificially burdens our health care spending much more than the legal systems other countries have in place.[170]

The great majority of injured patients do not sue their doctors, and only one in six of those who do sue receives compensation. In 40 percent of medical malpractice cases, there is no evidence of medical error or even that an injury has occurred. Yet these unquestionably frivolous lawsuits account for 16 percent of medical liability costs.[171]

Tort reform is a states-rights issue, and cost-cutting legal reforms should be enacted in every state. Meaningful caps on non-economic damages offer the main solution to our current legal award lottery and the drive by trial-level law firms to seek profits.

---

170 "Health care lawsuit reform in Washington State," by Roger Stark, Washington Policy Center, August, 2012 @ http://www.washingtonpolicy.org/publications/brief/health-care-lawsuit-reform-washington-state.

171 "Claims, Errors, and Compensation Payments in Medical Malpractice Litigation," by David M. Studdert, et. al., New England Journal of Medicine, 2006; 354(19): 2024–2033.

### Greater use of health savings accounts

Health Savings Accounts (HSAs) have been available since January 1, 2004.[172] At the time of their enactment, HSAs were highly controversial, with critics saying they would skim off the healthiest and wealthiest people, leaving older and sicker people to be covered by high-cost traditional insurance. This view held that HSAs would cause a "death spiral" or "race to the bottom" in the traditional health insurance market, driving up costs and greatly adding to the number of uninsured.

Although they were controversial at first, years of real-world experience shows that HSAs are a success, enjoy growing popularity, and have increasing enrollment with each passing year. HSA participants represent all socioeconomic levels in society, and consumer surveys show that owners are becoming informed users of health care. Surveys also show that most HSA owners are satisfied with their coverage and would not choose to go back to traditional third-party coverage.[173] Employees can take their HSAs from one job to another.

HSAs allow individuals more control over their health care expenses and thereby help hold down rising health care costs. An HSA comes with a high-deductible insurance plan, which functions as a catastrophic safety net. The insurance policy is coupled with a tax-free savings account that gives patients complete control over routine health care spending.

### Greater use of telemedicine

Certain geographic areas in the United States lack primary health care. These are mostly rural areas where patients have no timely

---

172 "Summary of HR 1, Medicare Prescription Drug Improvement, and Modernization Act, Public Law 108-173," CMS Legislative Summary, April 2004, www.cms.hhs.gov/MMAUpdate/downloads/PL108-173summary.pdf.

173 "BCBSA [Blue Cross Blue Shield Association] consumer Survey Shows High Rate of Satisfaction with HSAs, Cites Increased Reliance on Decision-Support Tools," BNET Business Network, U.S. Newswire, September 2005, at http://findarticles.com/p/articles/mi_hb5554/is_200509/ai_n21857463, and "High Deductible Health Plan Consumers Report Satisfaction, Higher Levels of Engagement of Health Care Choices," PRNewswireFirstCall, July 16, 2008, at www.tradingmarkets.com/.site/news/Stock%20News/1763222/.

access to doctors or physician extenders. Most of the anticipated physician shortage will occur in the primary care specialty, and rural communities will be adversely affected the most.

Telemedicine is defined as "the remote diagnosis and treatment of patients by means of telecommunication technology." Telemedicine can increase access to providers, which is the most important part of our health care system. Receiving timely care is critical to society having a healthy population. It gives patients choices in the type of care they obtain, and it gives providers more options to treat sick individuals. Diagnosing minor problems is much safer and less expensive than waiting for the patient's clinical condition to become severe.

Telemedicine can also decrease the costs of health care. A visit electronically can be much cheaper than a trip to the emergency room.

### Greater use of association health plans

Employers with a small number of employees have provided health benefits using association health plans (AHPs) for decades. AHPs allow small employers to join together to buy health insurance so their workers can gain access to the same pricing and coverage benefits enjoyed by large employers. Congress has a long history of support of AHPs.

AHPs can be organized in two ways. A consolidated AHP is underwritten at the group level, where all employees from all employers are placed in one plan. An affinity AHP is underwritten at the individual employee level. This can save money if the AHP has a much higher percentage of young and healthy workers. Both consolidated and affinity plans can either self-insure or can purchase health insurance from a commercial insurance company.[174]

Association health plans offer a real solution for small business

---

174 "Association health plans: What's all the fuss about?," by M.Kofman, K.Lucia, E.Bangit and K.Pollitz, Health Affairs, vol.25, no.6, pages 1591-1602, November, 2006 at https://www.venable. com/associationhealth-plans-and-health-care-reform-a-trap-for-the-unwary-04-22-2013/.

owners who want to provide employee health benefits. AHPs are based on voluntary associations, and they have a track record of offering quality health insurance at a reasonable price. Access to AHPs for any small business should be as easy as possible. Barriers to forming or joining an AHP should be minimal.

### State options for health care reform

- Section 1332 waivers[175]

Section 1332 waivers to the ACA can relieve states of the most harmful effects of the ACA, including the onerous premium price increases and the regulatory burden. The law states that "the Secretary shall determine the scope of a waiver" within the limits of "the authority of the Secretary."

- 1115A waivers

The federal government has allowed states to obtain Medicaid waivers since the beginning of the program. These waivers must follow strict guidelines, must be budget neutral, and are subject to federal oversight. In the past 50 years, the federal government has granted over 500 Medicaid waivers nationally.[176]

The ACA also expanded the use of 1115 Medicaid waivers by providing billions of federal taxpayer dollars for innovative, pilot projects. In order to be approved, these plans must reduce costs and improve health quality in the Medicaid program for the state making the application.[177]

---

175 "The Patient Protection and Affordable Care Act," Public Law 111-148, 111th Congress, pages 85-86, March 23, 2010, at https://www.gpo.gov/fdsys/pkg/PLAW-111publ148/pdf/PLAW-111publ148.pdf.

176 "State waiver list," federal Medicaid entitlement program, Medicaid.gov, August, 2017, at https://www.medicaid.gov/medicaid/section-1115-demo/demonstration-and-waiver-list/waivers_faceted.html.

177 "The Patient Protection and Affordable Care Act," Public Law 111-148, 111th Congress, pages 271-277, March 23, 2010, at https://www.gpo.gov/fdsys/pkg/PLAW-111publ148/pdf/PLAW-111publ148.pdf.

States could potentially use 1115 waivers to prioritize the use of Medicaid dollars to the truly needy and disabled, impose a work requirement where applicable, charge a small premium, require drug tests, and ultimately limit how long a person can be enrolled. Combining 1332 and 1115 waivers would also open up possibilities for broad-based health care reform at the state level.

- Pass state legislation to limit state taxpayers' contribution to the Medicaid expansion.

The ACA enticed states to expand Medicaid by offering federal taxpayer funds to cover 100 percent of the expansion costs for three years. After 2020, the states are required to pay ten percent of the costs. The federal government now has a $20 trillion debt, and there is a high likelihood that states will be required to pay more than ten percent of the Medicaid expansion cost in the future. State legislatures can pass laws that limit the amount of state taxpayer responsibility to ten percent or to a fixed amount of expansion costs.

- Repeal Certificate of Need laws.

Research now shows that state Certificate of Need laws do not decrease health care costs, but that they do limit patient choices by banning investment and construction of new health care facilities.

- Eliminate or decrease waste, fraud, and abuse in the Medicaid program.

A high percent of Medicaid costs do not increase care or access for enrollees. The massive bureaucratic nature of the program makes it a target for cheating and financial crime.

- Encourage home health care in the Medicaid program.

Costs are less and patient satisfaction is higher with home health care. It reduces government involvement in care and respects the natural family relationships of patients.

- Review scope-of-practice and licensing laws.

Most states will face a provider shortage to some degree in the near future. States should aggressively relax barriers to medical practice, which will increase access to health care for patients. Appropriate supervision of physician extenders is mandatory.

- Encourage direct primary care.

For a fixed amount of money per month, patients can access primary care around the clock. Direct primary care can increase access to doctors for all socioeconomic groups. Legislatures should protect direct primary care from state regulatory insurance laws.

The passage of the ACA has resulted in a huge increase in government control over our health care system, with a significant reduction in personal freedom and patient choice. Reforming or even repealing the ACA, while an improvement, would still leave the U.S. with a financially unsustainable system.

To control costs, increase choice, and maintain or improve quality, patients must be allowed to control their own health care dollars and make their own health care decisions. No third party, whether it is the government or an employer, is more concerned about a person's health than that person is. Patients, as health care consumers, should be allowed to be informed about, to review the prices of, and to gain access the best health care available in a fair, open, and free marketplace.

CHAPTER 20

# The Future of Health Care in the United States

M edical care in the United States has advanced tremendously over the past 100 years. From new antibiotics, to revolutionary cancer treatments, to surgical procedures that were unheard of a century ago, Americans today enjoy greater longevity and a better quality of life thanks to medical progress.

Health care policy has likewise changed dramatically over the past 100 years. Starting after the Revolutionary War, the federal government has provided health care benefits for military veterans. Government licensing of doctors began in the 1920s, and health insurance, along with its federal and state regulations, began in the 1930s. Changes to the federal tax code encouraged employers to pay for employee health benefits during World War II, a policy that is firmly entrenched in the U.S. today, with half of all Americans receiving their health insurance tax-free from their employer or spouse's employer.

A movement toward more government intervention and control of U.S. health care policy began early in the twentieth century and has persisted to this day. Medicare and Medicaid began in 1965 and were originally designed to be safety-net health insurance plans. The Affordable Care Act, or Obamacare, became law in 2010, while its provisions for Medicaid expansion and taxpayer subsidies in the individual insurance market followed in 2014. Today, over 40 percent of Americans are in one of these three government-managed insurance programs.

Although the government is expanding its control over the health care delivery system, America is still a very capitalistic country with the private, free-market sector of health care remaining viable at the present time. The question is what the future of the U.S. health care system will look like.

## Government programs

One out of every five Americans is enrolled in the Medicaid entitlement program. One out of every six is enrolled in the Medicare insurance program for seniors, and this number is growing as baby boomers retire. Politically, it is very difficult for lawmakers to reform or reduce benefits in any government entitlement. Essentially, once people receive an entitlement that feels free for the recipients, or at least is heavily subsidized, they and their political advocates strongly resist changes—even though those changes may guarantee the viability of that entitlement program.

Given this structural problem, what will the future of the government health care plans look like?

## Medicare

The federal Medicare program began in 1965 as health insurance for anyone the age of 65 or older. It is one of the largest social welfare programs in the world and functions essentially as a single-payer system. Workers pay a Medicare tax during their working years and then must enroll in government-provided health care after reaching the age of 65. The average worker uses three times as much health care as he or she had paid for during his or her working years.[178]

In 2018, 60 million people nationally (18 percent of the population) were enrolled in Medicare.[179] Total national spending on Medicare was nearly $750 billion in 2018.[180]

---

178  "Social Security and Medicare taxes and benefits over a lifetime, 2012 update," by C. Eugene Steuerle and Caleb Quakenbush, The Urban Institute, October 2012.

179  "CMS fast facts," Centers for Medicare and Medicaid Services, cms.gov, August 2018, at https://www.cms.gov/Research-Statistics-Data-and-Systems/Statistics-Trends-and-Reports/CMS-Fast-Facts/index.html.

180  See note #21.

Like Social Security, Medicare was intended to work as a pay-as-you-go system, in which current benefits are funded by current taxes. With the decreasing number of workers in the U.S. in future generations compared to the total population, and with the massive number of baby boomers approaching retirement age, this pay-as-you-go entitlement system is a fiscal catastrophe waiting to happen.

Medicare currently pays medical providers about 70 percent of what private insurance pays. A growing number of doctors say they are unable to see new Medicare patients and still pay their office overhead and expenses. This trend is increasingly limiting access to health care services for our seniors.

If Medicare is to continue in its present form, policymakers must take one or more of three possible steps: benefits will need to be decreased, payroll taxes will need to be increased, or seniors will need to pay more out of pocket. A fourth option would be to use general taxes to cover more of Medicare's yearly deficit. From an economic standpoint, none of these steps would predictably rein in the rising costs or decrease the demand for health care on the part of Medicare beneficiaries.

Even with these steps, there is virtually complete agreement that the federal Medicare program is not financially sustainable in its present form. The program's costs are rising, the number of workers paying monthly taxes into the program is proportionately decreasing, and the number of elderly recipients is about to increase dramatically as the baby boomer generation approaches age 65.

We now have an entire generation of people who has grown up with Medicare, have paid into it, and now expect full medical services in return. We also have people in younger generations who understand the bankrupt nature of the program and do not believe Medicare will still exist when they reach age 65.

A fair and workable solution to the Medicare problem must account for both of these generations, as well as provide reliable health coverage for future generations. As a country, we have a moral obligation to seniors already enrolled in the program and to those approaching retirement age.

The future of Medicare will depend on whether elected officials have the courage to reform the program in a sustainable fashion (see Chapter 6) or will simply continue down the present path, adding substantially to the national debt.

## Medicaid

The traditional Medicaid entitlement program was enacted in 1965 as part of the Medicare bill and provides both federal and state health care funding for poor children and their families, as well as for disabled individuals. It also provides long-term care. As part of the Affordable Care Act, states are allowed to expand their Medicaid programs to include any low-income, able-bodied adult.

As of August 2018, the Medicaid program covered 73 million individuals nationally.[181] It is the largest entitlement program in the world by enrollment and functions as a single-payer, government-controlled health insurance plan.

Although the expanded Medicaid program created under the ACA is largely funded by the federal government, approximately 40 percent of traditional Medicaid is funded by state taxpayers. Medicaid entitlement expenditures are the fastest growing budget items for virtually all states.

Doctor reimbursements in the program are 60 to 70 percent lower than what private insurance pays. Like Medicare, an increasing number of physicians are withdrawing from the program, saying the small government payments they receive are not enough to maintain their practices, which in turn sharply limits access to health care services for enrollees.

The cost of the Medicaid entitlement was $1 billion the first

---

181 "Medicaid and CHIP total enrollment chart – August 2018," at Medicaid.gov, August 2018, at https://www.medicaid.gov/medicaid/program-information/medicaid-and-chip-enrollment-data/report-highlights/total-enrollment/index.html.

year after enactment, and it had exploded to $577 billion by 2017.[182] At the present rate of growth, and even without considering the expansion created by the ACA, Medicaid entitlement costs will reach $700 billion a year by 2020.

State lawmakers are caught in a vicious cycle. The more state money they spend on Medicaid, the more federal money they receive from the national government, even though the cost is borne by their own constituents, who of course are also federal taxpayers.

Republican and Democrat lawmakers alike have voted to expand Medicaid well beyond the original safety-net entitlement. It is no surprise that the Medicaid program is the largest, fastest growing budget item for almost all states, and that it crowds out funding for other important government programs such as education and transportation.

There is growing interest to expand Medicaid further, to include, for example, funding for low-income housing and for food supplements.[183] The term "health" can be politically expanded to include a number of socioeconomic areas, and Medicaid dollars are very attractive for many forms of wealth redistribution. State officials like the federal matching money, and lawmakers like to give out apparently "free" benefits. Medicaid expansion could very well become the political platform for creating a single-payer system.

However, it is not too late to reform Medicaid. The most important first step to reforming and improving the program is to redesign it so it no longer functions as an open-ended entitlement. Welfare reform in the late 1990s, enacted under President Clinton, was successful because it targeted benefits and placed limits on how

---

182 "Total Medicaid spending," FY2017, The Henry J. Kaiser Family Foundation, at https://www.kff.org/medicaid/state-indicator/total-medicaid-spending/?currentTimeframe=0&sortModel=%7B%22colId%22:%22Location%22,%22sort%22:%22asc%22%7D.

183 "As part of push to treat 'whole person,' hospitals may be able to use Medicaid funds to pay for patients' housing, food," KHN Morning Briefing, Kaiser Health News, November 15, 2018, at https://khn.org/morning-breakout/as-part-of-push-to-treat-whole-person-hospitals-may-be-able-to-use-medicaid-funds-to-pay-for-patients-housing-food/.

many years people could expect government support. See Chapter 7 for Medicaid reform policies.

## The Affordable Care Act, or Obamacare

The Affordable Care Act (ACA) was passed into law with only Democratic votes in 2010. The main goals of the law were to slow the persistent rise in health care costs and to decrease the number of uninsured people in the U.S.

To date, 20 million people have obtained health insurance through Obamacare, with ten million people put into the expanded Medicaid program and ten million people receiving taxpayer subsidies in the exchanges.[184]

State taxpayers are also federal taxpayers. Consequently, as states expand their Medicaid programs under the ACA, their state taxpayers will ultimately be responsible for the entire cost of that expansion. Supporters of Obamacare would like to see further expansion of the Medicaid program to all states.

For political reasons, a public option was not included in the original ACA law. All Republican and many Democratic Members of Congress felt that placing a public option insurance plan in the exchanges would lead directly to a single-payer system.

A taxpayer-funded public option would devastate the private individual health insurance market and would potentially provide employers with essentially a "free" health insurance alternative for their employees. Yet many states are considering legislation to introduce a public option in the ACA exchanges. As the country learned with Medicare, it is impossible for private companies to compete with the government.

Both the expansion of Medicaid and the creation of a public-option health insurance plan would increase government involvement in the U.S. health care delivery system.

---

184 "Nearly 20 million have gained health insurance since 2010," by Nicholas Bakalar, *The New York Times*, May 22, 2017, at https://www.nytimes.com/2017/05/22/health/oba-macare-health-insurance-numbers-nchs.html

Congress was unable to repeal and replace the ACA in 2017. The longer an entitlement runs, the more accepting the American public becomes and the less likely lawmakers will be willing to remove the program.

The current federal administration has encouraged states to offer innovative alternatives to the ACA. The administration has also expanded the use of short-term, limited-duration health insurance plans and association health plans to decrease cost and increase access to health care for Americans.

## The Veterans Administration

The Department of Veterans Affairs (VA) is the second largest department in the federal government, serving nine million veterans with a budget of $200 billion per year.[185] Currently, the VA is a true socialized medicine program, with the government owning the hospitals and employing the doctors and staff. In one form or another, the department has been active since the Revolutionary War.

Quality and timeliness of care are not uniform in all VA facilities. Scandals have plagued the organization as veterans have been denied timely care and been placed on waiting lists. Privatization of parts or all of the system has been debated for years.[186] Privatization would allow veterans to obtain health care in the private, efficient marketplace, just as the majority of Americans do. Because of the unique needs of combat veterans and because of widespread support, the VA system will remain in place for the foreseeable future.

---

185 "We can fix veterans' health care without privatizing it," by N. Schlichting, *The Washington Post*, April 2, 2018, at https://www.washingtonpost.com/opinions/we-can-fix-veterans-health-care-without-privatizing-it-heres-how/2018/04/02/3b85a448-3443-11e8-8bdd-cdb33a5eef83_story.html?utm_term=.dbf96600ab24.

186 "Trump Administration plots costly private-care expansion for veterans," by Isaac Arnsdorf, Pro Publica, Inc., November 15, 2018 at https://www.propublica.org/article/trump-administration-plots-costly-private-care-expansion-for-veterans.

## Employer-paid health benefits

Employer-paid health insurance is unique to the United States and dates back to 1943. During World War II, the federal government imposed wage and price controls, but it did allow employers to offer tax-free benefits, including health insurance for employees. After the war, the wage and price controls were repealed, but the concept of tax-free employer-paid health insurance remained and has continued to the present time.[187]

Half of all Americans now receive their health care benefits from their employer or their spouse's employer. Although this arrangement has created a tax distortion and is one of the main reasons for job-lock (employees afraid to change jobs because they may lose health benefits), it currently enjoys widespread popularity. Employers often compete for workers based on the generosity of the health benefit plans they offer. Employers also benefit from the policy of a tax break for employee benefits, rather than paying workers higher taxable wages.

Employer-based health plans are also not subject to the ACA and state benefit mandates, but instead are governed by federal ERISA laws. The largest employers self-insure, while most smaller- and medium-sized employers use private, commercially-available insurance companies.

Employers are seeing their benefit costs go up and are shifting more financial responsibility to employees through the use of health savings accounts and high-deductible insurance plans. However, because of the popularity and the long-standing history of employer-paid health insurance, it will remain a major feature of the U.S. health care delivery system. It will also serve as a major deterrent to Congress imposing a national single-payer plan.

---

187 "Health care reform; lowering costs by putting patients in charge," by Roger Stark, MD, Policy Brief, Washington Policy Center, June 2015, at https://www.washingtonpolicy.org/library/docLib/Stark-_Health_care_reform_and_alternatives_to_the_Affordable_Care_Act.pdf.

## The individual health insurance market

The individual health insurance market is actually the smallest of all the health insurance markets in the U.S. The taxpayer-subsidized ACA exchanges have ten million enrollees, and the private individual market has an additional ten million participants.[188]

These 20 million people are affected the most by the changes in the health care system caused by Obamacare. The costs of insurance premiums are rising for all people in the U.S. (except for Medicaid enrollees), yet costs are rising much faster for people in the individual market.

The costly individual mandate in the ACA has caused young, healthy people to forgo the purchase of health insurance. They have made a reasonable economic decision that the government-approved health insurance is not worth the price to them, especially with the pre-existing condition mandate that forces insurance companies to sell policies after individuals become ill.

Consequently, the individual market is composed of an ever-increasing percentage of older, sicker people. Insurance companies have responded by raising premium rates and narrowing their provider networks. As premiums increase, the subsidies in the ACA exchanges increase as well. These increases in subsidies will keep the exchanges viable for the foreseeable future. The individual market outside the exchanges will likely collapse.

## Health insurance companies

Every year, millions of Americans buy auto, home, and life insurance from national companies in the competitive marketplace. People are savvy shoppers and have multiple choices when buying these types of insurances.

---

188 "20.1 million fewer Americans are uninsured post-health law, but coverage remains uneven," KHN Morning Briefing, Kaiser Health News, November 16, 2018, at https://khn.org/morning-breakout/20-1-million-fewer-americans-are-uninsured-post-health-law-but-coverage-remains-uneven/.

Insurance is defined as "a practice or arrangement by which a company or government agency provides a guarantee of compensation for specified loss, damage, illness, or death in return for payment of a premium."[189]

People often view health insurance differently than other types of insurance, however. When a person says he has "great health insurance," what he actually means is that his insurance covers nearly everything related to receiving health care, with essentially no out-of-pocket expense. Covered services can include dental treatment, eyewear, and routine visits to the doctor. This is analogous to a person having auto "insurance" that pays for routine maintenance services, including gas, oil, and brakes.

Obviously, the human body is different from a car or a house. However, from an insurance standpoint, which involves assessing and mitigating risk, health insurance should not be fundamentally different from auto or home-owners insurance.

The sale of health insurance began in the early 1900s in the U.S. and within several decades was accepted and well established. Many of the early health plans were set up as pre-payment for major medical expenses, similar to current health maintenance organizations (HMOs). Blue Cross, which pays hospitals, and Blue Shield, which pays doctors, began in the 1930s, and as non-profits both organizations have enjoyed a tax-free status since then.

Multiple private health insurance companies have been founded over the last 50 years. Consolidation among these companies is now occurring at a rapid pace.[190] A few private companies specialize in handling Medicaid patients for state governments.

---

189 "Is health insurance different than other types of insurance?," by Roger Stark, MD, Policy Note, Washington Policy Center, January, 2018, at https://www.washingtonpolicy. org/library/doclib/Stark-is-health-insurance-different-1.2018.pdf.

190 "What merger mania means for health care," by P. LaMonica, CNN Business, March 8, 2018, at https://money.cnn.com/2018/03/08/investing/health-care-mergers-cigna-ex-press-scripts-consolidation/index.html.

Health insurance companies are heavily regulated by the federal government and by state governments. The benefits provided by the insurance plans and the price of the plans are dictated by the government, so competition and consumer choice among companies is limited.

Most health insurance companies are reducing their participation in the individual market and are increasing their activity in the group or employer market, as well as the copay insurance market associated with Medicare.

The private insurance industry is a big part of health care in the U.S. It is well-financed and has a large political influence in Washington, D.C., as well as in every state capital. The industry will survive and will continue to play a major role in opposing adoption of a single-payer, government-run health care system.

## Hospitals and doctors

Hospital mergers and the salaried employment of doctors by hospitals are increasing at a rapid rate, leading to fewer doctors with independent practices.[191] This trend is driven by several factors.

Theoretically, hospital mergers should reduce costs by increasing centralized purchasing power. From an economic standpoint, however, reducing competition leads to monopoly-type pricing and less consumer choice, which actually increases costs.[192]

Medicare and Medicaid set provider reimbursement dollar amounts, and these are non-negotiable. Private insurance companies likewise negotiate fees and have followed the government programs in decreasing provider payments. Doctors are moving from

---

191 "How hospital merger and acquisition activity is changing healthcare," by J. LaPointe, Revcycle Intelligence, xtelligent Healthcare Media, 2017, at https://revcycleintelligence.com/features/how-hospital-merger-and-acquisition-activity-is-changing-healthcare.

192 "Monopolized healthcare market reduces quality, increases costs," by A. Kacik, Modern Healthcare, April 13, 2017, at https://www.modernhealthcare.com/article/20170413/NEWS/170419935.

independent practice to hospital employment to guarantee at least their base salaries, regardless of what the insurance plans pay. Hospitals employ doctors to lock in referral sources and to maintain a steady stream of patients.

The latest trend is more health insurance company involvement on the provider side of medicine. Insurance carriers are starting to employ doctors and buy outpatient clinical facilities outright rather than just paying patients' medical bills.[193] The economic motivator for insurance companies is greater cost containment since doctors in many cases drive health care costs by the number of tests and procedures they perform.

These company-owned health care models, a variation of health maintenance organizations (HMOs), have been tried in the past. Group Health Co-Operative was very active in Washington state until it was recently sold to Kaiser Permanente. Kaiser remains one of the premier HMOs in the country.

Experience with HMOs in the 1980s and 1990s showed that they can hold health care costs down. However, this was done with a gatekeeper system that tended to deny patients certain treatments and specialty referrals. HMOs were not popular with patients or doctors.

Over the past 20 years, medical care, when possible, has shifted to outpatient clinics. It is cheaper and easier for the patient to use an outpatient facility than to undergo the same procedure in a hospital. The time patients stay in the hospital has likewise been streamlined, and early discharge, when medically appropriate, is now common.

### Changes in physician training

Physician training after graduating from medical school is undergoing change as well. Limits have been placed on the number

---

193 "Reigniting the physicians arms race, insurers are buying practices," by S. Livingston, Modern Healthcare, June 2, 2018, at https://www.modernhealthcare.com/article/20180602/NEWS/180609985.

of hours a medical resident can work in any one week.[194] This model is gaining popularity for doctors employed by hospitals. Instead of one physician caring for a patient 24 hours a day, the trend is now for doctors to work shifts and pass care over to the doctor working the next shift. Quality of care may suffer under this arrangement.

All of these provider trends will continue into the foreseeable future.

## Health care lawsuit reform

Unlike other western countries, the United States has a very active legal system, and hospitals, doctors, and other health care providers must constantly manage the impending threat of costly medical lawsuits. In many states, health care lawsuit reform, that is, reasonable limits placed on the cost of a medical lawsuit, has helped hold costs down and provided a stable supply of skilled physicians in the area while still allowing wrongly injured patients to have their days in court.

The rise in the number of medical malpractice lawsuits has occurred in waves over the past 50 years. Three periods of crisis in soaring medical malpractice costs occurred in the 1970s, in the mid-1980s, and in the late 1990s to the mid-2000s. Malpractice insurance premiums for doctors fluctuate over time, but they predictably increase dramatically during these times of lawsuit crisis.[195]

The experience of several states, particularly Texas and California, shows that reasonable medical malpractice reform works. A meaningful legal cap on the amount of non-economic damages awarded by a court is the most effective element of successful

---

194 "ACGME duty hours are not the only big change in requirements," by B. Doolittle, MD, New England Journal of Medicine, NEJM+, May 25, 2017, at https://knowledgeplus.nejm.org/blog/acgme-duty-hours-not-the-only-big-change-in-requirements/.

195 "Health care lawsuit reform in Washington State," by Roger Stark, MD, Policy Brief, Washington Policy Center, August, 2012 at http://www.washingtonpolicy.org/ library/docLib/health-care-lawsuit-reform-washington-state-pb.pdf

lawsuit reform legislation. To a lesser extent, a reasonable statute of limitations on when lawsuits can be filed and pre-trial screening to weed out frivolous claims are often effective in reducing the cost of specific medical malpractice lawsuits.[196]

Officials in most states have been unable or unwilling to enact meaningful lawsuit reform, adding significantly to the rising cost of health care. Consequently, it has become a federal issue.[197] It is an uphill battle for Congress, however, because of the powerful trial lawyers' lobby, which encourages and profits from litigation, and the fundamental issue of states' rights. For these reasons, meaningful medical lawsuit reform is not likely to happen in the foreseeable future on a national scale and must be left to the individual states.

### Providing access to reliable and affordable pharmaceuticals

There is a great deal of confusion and misunderstanding in the United States about drug pricing, manufacturing, marketing, and the impact of government regulations.[198]

There is a growing opinion that the government should place a price control on pharmaceuticals. In 2014, prescription drug costs accounted for only 9.8 percent of overall health care expenses.

In economics, setting price limits on goods and services always results in scarcity, with less of the price-controlled product being produced and made available to consumers. This has been confirmed by the disastrous centrally planned economies of communist countries. Similar distorting effects and shortages would occur if

---

196 "Update on the cost of medical malpractice lawsuits in Washington state - lessons from Texas reform," by Roger Stark, MD, Policy Note, Washington Policy Center, April 11, 2016, at https://www.washingtonpolicy.org/library/doclib/Stark-Update-on-the-cost-of-medical-malpractice-lawsuits-in-Washington-State-Lessons-from-Texas-reform.pdf.

197 "Tort and litigation reform in the 115th Congress," by K. Lewis, Congressional Research Service, April 10, 2018, at https://fas.org/sgp/crs/misc/LSB10118.pdf.

198 "Prescription drug pricing – a complex, poorly understood issue," by Roger Stark, MD, Policy Note, Washington Policy Center, January 24, 2017, at https://www.washingtonpolicy.org/library/doclib/FINAL-PDF-drug-pricing-Roger.pdf.

government officials sought to control prescription drug prices in the United States.

If public officials really want to bring prices down and increase competition in the drug industry, they should streamline the government drug-approval process to reduce the time and money manufacturers devote to bringing a new medicine to market.

Depending on the study, the average cost of bringing a drug to market today is between $2.5 billion and $5 billion, and it takes from ten to 15 years to get through the government regulatory approval process.[199] There is even a backlog of generic drugs awaiting government approval; these are the medicines that have long been approved and available in patent form. The current Food and Drug Administration is trying to reduce these regulatory barriers and is working to speed up the drug-approval process.

Drug pricing is a complex process that involves not only research and development costs, but also is distorted by third-party payers such as insurance plans and by pharmaceutical benefit managers. Rather than dealing with the entire process and removing complexity and waste, it is easier and more politically attractive for elected officials to simply demand that the government impose price controls on drugs.

As a result, patients in the U.S. may very well experience price controls on medications in the future, beginning with people in the Medicare and Medicaid entitlement programs.

**Innovative and free-market ideas**

The United States has the most vibrant and innovative economy in the world. It has an abundance of entrepreneurs who work hard to make life better for people. In spite of government regulations and control, free-market ideas continue to percolate up to become reality and provide better access to health care at lower costs for patients.

---

199 "Cost to develop new pharmaceutical drug now exceeds $2.5 B," by Rick Mullen, *Scientific American*, November 24, 2014 at https://www.scientificamerican.com/article/cost-to-develop-new-pharmaceuticaldrug-now-exceeds-2-5b/

Following are examples of how free-market creativity is improving the delivery of quality health care.

## Affordable direct primary care

Many primary care doctors have become tired of government regulations, paper work, and ever-decreasing payments from Medicare and Medicaid. They have elected to practice medicine without the hassles of dealing with insurance companies—both private and government plans.

Doctors who have direct primary care (DPC) practices offer patients 24-hour access to a primary care physician for a fixed monthly price. DPC began as an alternative for wealthy patients (then called "concierge medicine"), but it has become affordable and has expanded into the Medicaid population.[200] Patients still need to have a major medical insurance plan to cover hospitalizations, but patients can access all routine primary care directly with an independent doctor using DPC.

The use of DPC is growing and is a viable and affordable option for millions of Americans.

## Telemedicine

Early reports show that patient and physician satisfaction is high with telemedicine. However, the different guidelines imposed by the various insurance programs, both public and private, is an ongoing administrative problem for providers. The use of telemedicine will increase in the future as data and communication costs fall and as patients become more familiar with the technology.

## Alternative health coverage programs

Faith-based, or "health sharing ministries," allow people of the same religion to form a health insurance co-op. These plans are

---

200 "Qliance; a revolution in primary care," by E. Bliss, MD, Washington Policy Center presentation, June 3, 2009, at https://www.washingtonpolicy.org/library/docLib/erika_bliss_presentation_wpc_09.pdf.

not true insurance and are not regulated by the ACA, so they are free of the many costly benefit mandates required by Obamacare. Consequently, they are cheaper than traditional health insurance.[201]

They function similarly to traditional insurance, although these plans do not necessarily have a large "reserve" of money. Instead, they "share" health care costs among plan members. Confidence in these plans is growing, as they demonstrate their value and reliability in paying for life's unpredictable medical expenses. There are currently fewer than ten ministries throughout the country, but this number is predicted to increase.

A similar plan to faith-based ministries is a start-up company called Health and Prosperity Partnerships for Everyone or HAPPE. It is essentially a non-religious, voluntary co-op in which members share health care costs. If successful, the concept could provide an affordable alternative to traditional insurance for individuals, as well as for employees in large-group employer plans.

Voluntary, alternative health coverage options can thrive, provided that bureaucrats do not impose a heavy government regulatory burden on the plans.

## Technology innovations

As in so many areas of our daily lives, the boom in technology potentially offers patients more control over their health care at greatly reduced costs. For example, there are currently dozens of smartphone apps for both providers and patients that offer more information in a timelier fashion than traditional medical devices.[202] Competition in the free market is holding down the cost of these innovations.

---

201 "What is faith-based healthcare?," by J. Mendelowitz, HealthCare.com, September 24, 2017, at https://www.healthcare.com/info/obamacare-alternatives/what-is-faith-based-healthcare.

202 "20 hot apps for healthcare providers," by F. Bazzoli, Health Data Management, September 4, 2018, at https://www.healthdatamanagement.com/list/20-notable-apps-for-provider-organizations.

For doctors, hospitals, and clinics, research and development have made traditional medical devices smaller, more affordable, and more user-friendly. For example, sonogram imaging machines, once large, expensive, and cumbersome, are now more affordable, produce higher-quality images, and are portable.

No one can predict the number of innovations that will be available in the future. The marketplace, through patient experiences, should determine the value of the innovations, not government officials imposing regulations based on the vague guesses they make about future technology.

## A two-tiered health care system

There is a possibility that health care in the U.S. will evolve into a two-tiered system. Medicare, Medicaid, the individual market in the Obamacare exchanges, and the Veterans Administration system together now provide health insurance for over 40 percent of Americans. Alternatively, 50 percent of Americans receive their health insurance from their employer or their spouse's employer in a heavily regulated private market.

Before the Medicare and Medicaid law was passed in 1965, communities had charity or county hospitals that provided free and reduced-priced care to low-income people. Patients received excellent care in these facilities, albeit in a multi-bed ward setting with many medical interns and residents providing the care. Many of these hospitals still exist and continue to handle a large portion of Medicaid patients and trauma victims. Before 1965, private hospitals treated patients with private insurance or those who paid out of pocket.

Today, private hospitals treat patients who do not have government insurance, Medicare patients, and some Medicaid enrollees. These private facilities compete for patients by offering single-patient rooms, new or remodeled structures, and amenities for patients' families.

Because of the inefficient third-party payer system in U.S. health care (regardless of whether the payer is the government or the patient's employer), patients are isolated from the true costs of their hospital care. Consequently, hospitals have very little incentive to compete on the cost of care.

If patients were paying for their own care, it is conceivable that the hospitals would compete not only on quality, but also on price. This is exactly what occurs in other economic activities. Not everyone owns or wants a Lexus, and not everyone wants to eat steak every night. Hospitals currently have so much invested in the modernization trend, and the third-party payer system is so firmly engrained in the health care system that a return to private plus public hospitals will probably not happen.

The government would need to deregulate the private health insurance industry for a two-tiered system to work effectively. Patients can now obtain and pay out of pocket for health care outside of the hospital setting. In-hospital care, however, can be very expensive, and for most patients requires insurance coverage. There is currently very limited enthusiasm for reducing costs through health insurance deregulation.

On the other hand, patient care outside of the hospital setting is already forming a two-tiered system through the growth of direct primary care as well as technological innovations.

It is nearly impossible to repeal an entitlement once the government has enacted it, gotten people dependent on it, and attracted powerful interest groups to defend and expand it. For example, Medicare is not financially sustainable in its present form. Yet, even the idea of gradual reform of the program is extremely unpopular with seniors and their political advocates. This creates an atmosphere in which a thoughtful debate is almost impossible. The same is true of reform or replacement of Medicaid and the taxpayer subsidies in the Obamacare exchanges.

Consequently, it appears that the government health care entitlements are here to stay and will probably expand in the future. A fully socialist single-payer system is now a stretch too far for most Americans. However, an incremental movement toward a single-payer system is not only possible but is also being advocated by many on the political left. By dropping the age of eligibility for Medicare, by offering a pubic option in the ACA exchanges, by shifting more people into Medicaid, and by allowing people to buy into Medicare or Medicaid, the country could gradually move toward a single-payer, government system by default.

Employer-paid health insurance remains popular, is well accepted in the U.S., and has a 75-year history. It will continue for the foreseeable future. On the other hand, if premiums for employers continue to increase, more costs may shift to employees. Ultimately, employers, especially small- and medium-sized companies, may drop employee health benefits completely.

Existing health insurance carriers, drug manufacturers, and medical device companies are extremely well financed. They will remain in place. New companies in these fields will find a difficult time getting established in the current financial and regulatory climate, unless they are purchased early by an existing company.

Private health care, outside of the insurance market, will continue to grow through technological innovations, health savings accounts, and direct primary care. New insurance models, such as HAPPE and faith-based plans, will thrive if protected from government interference, but they will still represent a small portion of total health care delivery.

In general, the country appears to be moving gradually, but persistently, toward a socialized single-payer health care system. The greatest unknown factor looking ahead is how Americans who are not currently dependent on government insurance plans and who benefit from good-quality private coverage will respond to even greater political control over their health care.

Free-market solutions do exist. To control costs, increase choice, and maintain or improve quality, patients should be allowed to control their own health care dollars and make their own health care decisions. No third party, whether it is the government or an employer, is more concerned about a person's health than that person is. Patients, as health care consumers, should be allowed to be informed about, to review the prices of, and to gain access to the best health care available in a fair, open, and free marketplace.[203]

---

203 "Health care reform: Lowering costs by putting patients in charge," by Roger Stark, MD, Policy Brief, Washington Policy Center, July 6, 2015, at https://www.washingtonpolicy.org/publications/detail/health-care-reform-lowering-costs-by-putting-patients-in-charge.

CHAPTER 21

# Selected Opinion Editorials

O pinion articles provide timely commentary on relevant policy issues. They reflect the opinion of the author and are based on facts and provable data. I include these op-eds to give the reader a sense of the evolution of health care policy over the past few years. Most of these issues remain pertinent today. In many cases, these items have already been addressed so far, but more detail can be found in this chapter.

Some of the following have been published nationally in *The Washington Examiner, Forbes, The Federalist, American Spectator,* and *The Washington Times.* Others included here have been published regionally in *The Seattle Times, The Puget Sound Business Journal, The Spokesman Review, The Everett Herald,* as well as many local newspapers.

## Health Care Costs
*September 15, 2008*

The fundamental problem with the health care system in this country is the cost. We spend 17 percent of our gross domestic product, or nearly $2.2 trillion, on health care each year in the United States. Most proposals to reform health care delivery offer a way to control these expenses through the use of more regulations, "better" medicine, and ultimately, a government-managed system.

There is an economic principle at work here, that like gravity, cannot be ignored or dismissed. The principle is that costs will continue to increase as long as someone else pays for our health care. Whether it is a government agency or an employer, a third party is now paying for over 87 percent of the health care in this country, even as individual copays and deductibles are increasing. As long as someone else is picking up the tab, demand and utilization will far outstrip the supply. This is an economic law, and it must be addressed before any reform will work.

Let's say you were going to build a new airplane but didn't worry about the law of gravity. Regardless of how you designed the plane, or how much technology you put into the aircraft, or how large you made the engine, if you neglected to consider that the plane must overcome gravity, the project will fail.

This is exactly what health care reformers are doing when they propose plans that ignore the economic law that states an individual will demand many more health services as long as someone else is paying the bill.

Obviously, employers mean well when their goal is a healthy work force, and they feel obligated to provide health care benefits for their employees to remain competitive. Similarly, the politicians who support government-run health care undoubtedly believe that a centrally planned system is the best and most efficient. Yet imagine what would happen if the government or our employer paid for our food, shelter, and clothing, which like health care, are other necessities of life. Demand would far outstrip supply, and some form of rationing would need to take place. Of course, the payer would then make the rationing decisions, and the individual recipient would be totally dependent on the payer for the amount and quality of food, clothing, and shelter he or she would receive.

Only when individuals can direct their own medical spending through a market will costs become transparent and likewise come under control. Critics have said that health care is too important and too complex to be left to individuals. Yet health care is simply an economic activity, and because of its complex nature, can only be managed through the unregulated interaction of providers and patients. We have learned over the past century that government central planning is doomed to fail (witness the Soviet Union and Eastern Europe) and only leads to supply-and-demand mismatches, lack of goods and services, and ultimately rationing.

Americans are the smartest shoppers in the world. We are extremely knowledgeable when it comes to buying virtually every service or product offered in our economy—except for health care. There is absolutely no reason to believe we would not become savvy purchasers of health-related services if we were spending our own dollars. Through the use of the Internet, consumer reports, and word of mouth, Americans can obtain the proper type and amount of health care that they need, without interference from employers or the government.

When anyone proposes health care reform, the first and most important question to ask is who is the payer for this health care. If it is not the patient, the reform is doomed to fail and will lead to overutilization, uncontrolled spending, and ultimately, to some form of rationing.

## What Is *NOT* Wrong With U.S. Health Care
*March 23, 2009*


Change is coming to the health care system in this country. At $2.1 trillion per year, or 17 percent of our Gross Domestic Product (GDP), cost should be the driver for this movement to reform our current system.

As the debate continues on in the next few months, however, a number of other arguments will be used to indict our present mix of public and private programs. Many of these arguments are based on a faulty presentation of the facts, so let's look at the actual data and see what is *not* wrong with our health care system

First, we hear a lot about how terrible the infant mortality rate is in the United States, supposedly the worst in the civilized world. Is this true? Not really. U.S. health officials count *all* live births, while many other countries only count full-term births or infants who live at least 28 days. Obviously, premature infants, who are counted in the U.S. but not in other countries, have a much higher risk of mortality.

Second, we are told people in the U.S. don't live as long as people in other countries. However, deaths from homicide and accidents distort the picture. When the data is adjusted for these categories, life expectancy in the U.S. is as high as in other countries. Homicide and violent trauma certainly reflect a country's social problems, but they tell us little about its health care system.

Third, we are told that each year in the U.S. there are nearly 100,000 unnecessary hospital deaths. A panel of doctors reviewed the hospital data and found the great majority of these deaths occur at the end of the patient's natural life, when the outcome would have been the same regardless of what hospital staff did or did not do. In other countries, these older, desperately ill people might not even be sent to a hospital, dying at home instead, and are thus not included in national medical statistics.

A comparable, population-adjusted study in Canada found

200,000 "unnecessary" hospital deaths, even though political activists regularly push Canadian-style health care as the model for the U.S.

Fourth, we hear people are often forced to declare bankruptcy because of medical bills. It turns out advocates count *any* bankruptcy case involving even a single medical bill, whether or not health costs had anything to do with causing the bankruptcy.

Also, people ages 55 to 65, who have more personal control over their health coverage, are *less* likely to declare bankruptcy, while people over 65, who are on government-run Medicare, have seen a doubling of their bankruptcy rate. In the case of the elderly, tax-funded health care has not reduced bankruptcies for older Americans.

Fifth, we are told 45 million Americans are uninsured. Who are the uninsured? Is cost really the reason they do not have coverage? It turns out political advocates count anyone who was without health coverage *at any time* during a calendar year. Half of those counted as uninsured were in transition to a new job, and one-third could sign up for a government program (like Medicare, Medicaid, or state-subsidized care) but choose not to.

Only about eight million people, less than five percent of Americans, are chronically uninsured. This is a serious problem, but hardly a reason to revolutionize health coverage for 95 percent of the population.

Sixth, we are told the U.S. ranks a dismal thirty-seventh in health care worldwide. The figure comes from the U.N.'s World Health Organization. Three of the five criteria used to rate nations were biased in a favor of nationalized, single-payer systems, and U.N. officials admit they have an 80 percent uncertainty level in their data. Amazingly, *none* of the five criteria included actual health outcomes, such as cancer or heart attack survival rates.

Because the U.S. does not have total, nationalized health care, our system was severely disadvantaged before the study began. Any health study that ranks Greece (#14), Columbia (#22), and Morocco (#29) ahead of the U.S. clearly has methodological problems.

The national debate about how to improve health care needs honest research accurately presented, not skewed data or false comparisons with other countries. The six myths about U.S. health care only serve to shift our focus away from the real problem: overregulation and artificially high costs. Only when public policy reconnects patients with their own health care dollars, and when decisions about care are made by doctors talking with patients, not by government program managers, will our nation be in a position to control costs and extend coverage to the chronically uninsured.

## Looming Doctor Shortage is One More Example
## Why Central Planning Doesn't Work in Health Care
*December 6, 2011*

The U.S. in general, and Washington state in particular, are facing a severe doctor shortage in the next ten to 15 years. Not only is the population growing, but the baby boomer generation is aging and will require more medical services in the near future.

Also, the new federal health care law will give health insurance to 30 million previously uninsured people over the next few years. These millions of newly insured patients will further strain our stretched provider network.

In 2010, there were 27.7 doctors per 10,000 people in the U.S. and 27.0 per 10,000 people in Washington. Medical schools graduated 16,838 students nationally in 2010, and the University of Washington, our state's only traditional medical school, graduated 169. Washington has a new osteopathic school in Yakima that will graduate its first class of 75 students next year.

The Association of American Medical Colleges anticipates a shortage of 150,000 doctors in the next 15 years. The Bureau of Labor Statistics predicts a need for 145,000 new doctors by 2018. Our state will potentially face a shortage of 3,000 to 4,000 doctors over the next ten to 15 years.

For years the government has controlled the number of medical schools, the number of graduates from these schools and their licensure. This has created a distortion in the supply of health care. Government central planners are even attempting to legislate not only the total number of doctors, but also the number of primary care physicians and the number of specialists in the country. This is as futile and absurd as the government telling people how many laptop versus desktop computers we need. No amount of information or analysis will enable central planners to know how many doctors, and of what type, the country needs.

The government has imposed central planning on the demand side of our health care system as well.

Starting in 1943, the federal government allowed employers to take a business-income tax deduction for the costs of employee health benefits. Individuals, however, were not allowed to take this same tax deduction. This was the beginning of the U.S. employer-financed health insurance model. In 1965, Congress passed Medicare and Medicaid entitlements into law, which placed millions of people into government-financed health insurance. The U.S. now has a health care system in which 85 percent of the costs are paid by a disinterested third party—either the employer or the government. It has become very rare for patients to take responsibility for the total cost of their own medical care.

This government-planned, third-party payment system has created ingrained market distortion and has caused an excessive demand in health care. After all, when someone else pays, there is no incentive for patients to question the price or quantity of services that are consumed in their care. In this situation, prices soar and goods and services are heavily overutilized.

The advantage of an open market is that resources are constantly adjusted and balanced so that supply consistently equals demand. As demand fluctuates, supply will increase or contract to meet consumers' needs. In health care, demand is set by the patients, and supply is a function of the number of doctors and their availability.

Only when patients can control their own health care dollars can the demand be correctly determined. The necessary and sufficient number of doctors each community needs can only be known through millions of routine, voluntary actions made in the free market.

## Solutions to Our Health Care Crisis
*Feb 17, 2012*

The fundamental problem with the health care system in this country is its ever-rising cost. We spend 17 percent of our gross domestic product, or nearly $2.5 trillion, on health care each year. Most policy proposals attempt to control these expenses by imposing more top-down regulations, "better" medicine, and ultimately, a government-managed system.

Costs will continue to increase as long as each of us believes someone else will pay for our health care. Whether it is a government agency or an employer, a third party is now paying over 87 percent of health care costs, even as individual copays and deductibles are increasing. As long as we think someone else is picking up the tab, demand and utilization will far outstrip supply. This is an immutable economic law and it must be addressed before any reform will work.

Only when people can direct their own medical spending through a free market will costs become transparent and likewise come under control. Critics say health care is too important and too complex to be left to mere individuals. Yet health services are like any other economic activity, and because of their highly complex nature, they can only be managed through the unregulated interaction of providers and patients.

Unless patients can control their own health care dollars, reform is doomed to fail and will lead to overutilization, uncontrolled spending, and ultimately to some form of medical rationing.

At present, there are five solutions to our current health care problem:

### 1. Change the Tax Code

Congress should change the federal tax code and allow individuals to deduct their health expenses, just as businesses and privately insured self-employed individuals do. This would give employees the freedom to purchase their own insurance and would allow employers to decrease their overhead and offer higher wages.

Individual insurance coverage, not tied to employment, would also allow people to keep their health care coverage as they move from job to job and state to state.

Why should an employer provide health benefits in the first place? Why not simply adjust wages upward and allow employees to buy their own individual plans? Except for retirement plans, there are very few other needs in life (like food or housing) that are provided by employers.

### 2. Eliminate Some State Mandates

Mandates set by state policymakers now restrict patient choice in the purchase of individual health insurance. Instead of offering people a range of choices, mandates require all individual plans to provide the same benefits and increase costs for everyone. For example, why should a 25-year-old single man be forced to pay for obstetrical coverage?

Mandates are the classic example of politically powerful lobby groups inducing legislators to include their services in every insurance policy. Washington state has 58 mandates, whereas Idaho has 17.

A reasonable first step would be to allow interstate commerce in health insurance. People could then purchase any approved insurance plan from any company in any state. Literally overnight, consumers would have a huge increase in personal choices, and the market would become much more competitive.

### 3. Reform Medicare and Medicaid

The non-partisan Congressional Budget Office reports the Medicare program is not financially sustainable in its present form. Costs are rising, the number of workers to support the program is proportionately decreasing, and the number of recipients is about to increase dramatically as baby boomers reach retirement.

We now have an entire generation that has grown up with Medicare, has paid into it, and expects something in return. We also have young people who understand the bankrupt nature of the program and do not believe Medicare will exist when they reach age 65.

The solution must account for young people and the elderly, as well as for future generations. We have a moral obligation to the seniors already enrolled in the program and those approaching retirement. Simple first steps to fixing Medicare would be to raise the age of eligibility to 68 or 70 years and to require means testing for enrollment.

Future generations should be allowed to take their individual health care insurance into retirement and not be forced into a government program. No surprise, younger people as a group are healthier than older people, so as the younger generation saves, their health care insurance nest egg can build until they need it in later years.

Medicaid, the program for poor families, is in the same unsustainable financial condition as Medicare—perhaps worse. We must care for the poor, but giving them mandated, unlimited, first-dollar coverage is both financially and ethically unsound. A voucher system allowing personal choice and a financial reward for dollars saved would be an excellent start to solving Medicaid's problems.

States should also receive Medicaid waivers and block grants from the federal government. States could budget more efficiently with a fixed yearly amount of money rather than the open-ended entitlement of the current Medicaid program. They could also design their own innovative programs without being stopped by the federal government.

States should be allowed to return to the original income requirement of 133 percent of the federal poverty level for their Medicaid recipients, instead of the 250 to 300 percent they now use.

## 4. Enact Tort Reform

Nearly 20 percent of our health care budget is spent on the legal system through attorney fees, court costs, malpractice insurance premiums, and most importantly, defensive medicine. Medical outcomes in the U.S. are no worse, and in many ways much better, than in other countries, yet our legal system burdens doctors and hospitals much more than the legal systems in other countries.

Meaningful caps on non-economic damages offer the main solution to our current legal awards lottery.

## 5. Make Health "Insurance" True Risk-Management Insurance

We also need to fundamentally change how we view health insurance. Instead of "insurance" paying for every health-related activity, it needs to work like other forms of risk-management insurance, such as car and homeowner's insurance.

Just as no one uses insurance to pay for gas or to mow the lawn, we need to get away from the idea of health insurance covering all minor health-related events. True indemnity insurance should be there for catastrophes and emergencies. Day-to-day health expenses should be paid out of pocket.

An effective mechanism to do this today is a health savings account (HSA). These are being used by an increasing number of Americans. HSAs require a person or family to purchase a high-deductible catastrophic policy but allow a tax-advantaged savings account for day-to-day medical purchases. Savings can be rolled over from year to year and can be taken from one job to another.

These five solutions offer the best way out of our health care crisis. Patients, acting as health care consumers, would demand more transparency in pricing and, just as happens in other areas of life, would force competition, improve quality and service, and drive costs down.

## Limiting Lawsuit Costs Would Make
## Health Care More Affordable
*September 26, 2012*

Everyone agrees the rising cost of health care in the United States is unsustainable. Last year, Americans spent $2.4 trillion, or nearly 18 percent of our gross domestic product, on health care. Frivolous lawsuits against doctors and hospitals contribute significantly to these rising costs, with estimates as high as ten to 20 percent of added health care costs caused by the legal system.

In many states, health care lawsuit reform, that is, reasonable limits placed on the cost of lawsuits, has helped hold costs down and provided a stable physician pool, while still allowing injured patients to have their day in court. Medical malpractice reform was the number-one health care reform recommended by our state's small-business owners at Washington Policy Center's 2011 Small Business Conference.

The number of medical malpractice suits has occurred in waves over the past 50 years. Three crises in soaring medical malpractice costs occurred in the 1970s, the mid-1980s, and the late 1990s into the mid-2000s.

The great majority of injured patients do not sue their doctors, and only one in six of those who do sue receives compensation. In 40 percent of medical malpractice cases, there is no evidence of medical error or even that an injury has occurred.

Unfortunately, the patient is not the biggest winner in the dispersal of high-dollar jury awards. Patients, on average, receive only 46 percent of the money they are awarded by juries. The remainder goes to lawyers, expert witnesses, and court fees. The average time an injured patient waits to receive compensation is five years.

Although gross negligence does sometimes occur in health care, just as often doctors get sued merely for bad patient outcomes. Patient expectations can often be unreasonably high, or the physician has not spent enough time discussing the severity of the patient's condition and the, possibly low, chances of recovery. When dealing with the human body, a less than ideal outcome often results, despite the best care modern medicine can provide.

Court cases are usually determined by the testimony of expert witnesses. An entire industry of professional experts has grown up, although qualifications for experts continue to evolve. Today, experts can be hired to argue virtually any side in a pending lawsuit.

Ideally, irresponsible doctors are sanctioned with practice limitations imposed by their medical peers or, when necessary, have their licenses revoked. Ironically, it is lawyers, working on behalf of and protecting bad doctors, who make it difficult for medical associations to police chronically bad physicians. Hospital and community medical review committees continually face the threat of civil lawsuits over defamation of character or restraint of trade when they try to weed out bad doctors.

The experience of other states shows that a meaningful legal cap on non-economic damages is the most effective element of successful lawsuit reform legislation. For example, the California legislature passed a cap on non-economic damages in 1975, and since then, the state has experienced a stable physician pool and stable malpractice insurance premiums.

The barriers to enacting non-economic caps are provisions in some state constitutions, the active political opposition of powerful state trial lawyer associations, and the question of whether the states or the federal government should pass such legislation. To control the rise in medical lawsuit costs, Washington state would need to amend its constitution. This would require a supermajority of legislative votes as well as supermajority support of voters. This reform should be enacted to avoid the next medical malpractice crisis in our state.

In addition, meaningful caps on non-economic damages would encourage more doctors to stay in practice in Washington, would promote greater expertise in key medical specialties, and would make the state a more attractive place for University of Washington Medical School graduates and doctors from other states to open their practices here. This reform would improve the affordability and quality of health care for all Washington residents.

## Is Being Put on Medicaid Better Than Having No Insurance?
### *September 9, 2013*

Does being put on Medicaid, the government's entitlement program for the poor, actually save lives or improve people's health? This is a question that has not been answered until very recently.

In 2008, Oregon lawmakers decided they had enough additional public money to put 10,000 more people on the state's Medicaid program. So, Oregon officials held a lottery that ultimately signed up 6,400 new Medicaid enrollees. A further 5,800 people were eligible for the program but were not selected. People in this group had the same health and economic profile as the lottery winners, allowing researchers to make valid comparisons. This created the perfect test-case on the effectiveness of Medicaid in providing care. These 5,800 people became the control group in an objective, randomized health care study.

The *New England Journal of Medicine* recently reported the results. The conclusion is surprising. It turns out that being put on Medicaid does not improve health outcomes, nor does it improve mortality statistics, compared to having no insurance coverage at all. The Medicaid group had no improvement in the important objective measurements of blood sugar levels, blood pressure, and cholesterol levels. The study did find that vaguely defined "mental health" was improved; however, this was done via subjective telephone interviews, not objective clinical data. For those few people requiring prolonged medical and hospital treatment, Medicaid did improve the financial status of those patients because their medical bills were covered by federal and Oregon taxpayers.

The existing Medicaid program has 60 million enrollees nationally at a cost of $430 billion per year. Looking forward, the cost is estimated to increase to $900 billion a year by 2019, yet the study indicates the health status of people put on Medicaid is not better than the uninsured population.

Medicaid is an extremely inefficient program, and reimbursement for doctors and other providers is about half of what private insurance pays for the same services. Doctors are not able to pay their own overhead with these low payment rates, and, consequently, our existing Medicaid patients have trouble accessing health care.

The Washington State Medical Association recently found 18 percent of primary care providers had dropped all Medicaid patients, and 24 percent were not taking new Medicaid patients because of poor payment and the complexity of treating Medicaid patients compared to privately insured patients. Getting access to health care is a significant problem for people in the existing Medicaid program in our state. It turns out having "insurance" is not the same as actually seeing a doctor.

The Affordable Care Act, or Obamacare, gives states the option to expand Medicaid to at least 16 million new patients nationally and 280,000 in Washington state. The law says that any adult over the age of 18 who earns less than 138 percent of the federal poverty level can be put on Medicaid. The estimated cost to taxpayers of this expansion is at least $450 billion over the first ten years, starting in 2014.

The Oregon study confirms that Medicaid does not provide better health care to people than having no insurance at all. These terrible results not only come with a huge taxpayer cost, but also trap poor individuals in a virtually worthless health insurance plan.

The Washington State Legislature has expanded Medicaid largely because the federal government has bribed the states with federal taxpayer money. Many of our state legislators supported the expansion because it felt like "free" federal money, and because they reasoned putting people into Medicaid is better than being uninsured. The large, randomized Oregon study shows this is not true.

Of course, state taxpayers are also federal taxpayers, so ultimately the people of Washington state will pay for this Medicaid expansion. Medicaid is a pay-as-you-go program. The idea of leaving free federal money "on the table" makes no sense. If Medicaid doesn't expand, the burden of taxes should be reduced for everyone.

Our legislators would do better to improve the existing Medicaid program, eliminate waste, fraud and abuse, improve access and make the program a real safety-net health insurance plan that provides quality at a reasonable cost.

## The Facts About Class Envy and Income Inequality
*March 17, 2014*

President Obama and activists on the left would like to use the topic of income inequality as a campaign issue in 2014 and probably in the 2016 elections. They say that the rich are getting richer, the poor are getting poorer, and the middle class is shrinking, and that's why we should calmly accept their political plans to expand the reach of government power into lives of all Americans.

A superficial interpretation of statistics might appear to support this argument, but a careful analysis of income data over the past 60 years absolutely refutes the idea of growing income inequality. Statistics are excellent for proving a snapshot of a fixed point in time, but they fail miserably at tracking real individuals as they move among the various economic brackets during their working and retirement years. A person might sell a house and be "rich" for one year, working professionals may have a good income year followed by several lean years, or a person may be "rich" until the day they retire and the next day become someone with zero earned income.

Research shows that 75 percent of people in the bottom 20 percent of income in 1975 were in the top 40 percent within 16 years.

Income statistics do not account for dollar transfers. Millions of people receive health benefits, food stamps, and housing subsidies. None of this is counted as income. Studies show that personal income accounts for only 22 percent of economic resources available to those in the bottom 20 percent. Workers today receive more in non-wage benefits than in past generations.

Are the poor getting poorer? Income statistics only measure cash. They don't look at people's true standards of living. The bottom 20 percent today have most of the good things a middle class family had 40 years ago, including color TVs, air conditioning, microwaves, and cars.

Exaggerated claims about income inequality also don't include an individual's real net worth or potential earning capacity. Statistics about the "poor" include retirees, non-working spouses of the rich, professionals just starting out in practice, and young adults. These people hardly fit the picture of the working poor.

Most statistics do not look at the differences between full and part time or no employment. Less than one half of people considered poor work at all, and less than three percent work full time. Although the country in general has more part-time workers, the vast majority of those in the top 20 percent work full time.

We also hear that the middle class is shrinking. This argument uses a fixed, average income from years ago as a reference mark. Overall, incomes have increased, even when adjusted for inflation, so the original "average" is obviously lower and applies to fewer people. A fixed definition of income classes does not reflect the true dynamic income picture. The middle class in the U.S. is as large and vibrant as ever.

One of the greatest attributes of the U.S. is the ability of people to better themselves and move up the economic ladder. The vast majority of the rich earned their success. The economy is not a zero-sum game, it's about growth and opportunity for everyone.

There are two solutions to help the poor. First, an education is vitally important. In the top 20 percent of income earners, 60 percent have college degrees compared to six percent in the bottom 20 percent. Second, a vibrant, growing economy helps people improve in all economic brackets.

The U.S. economy is not about government officials picking winners and losers. It is about people having the ability to improve their financial status through hard work in a free and open society. Pushing the political idea of wealth redistribution is not an effective or moral way to help the poor.

## Does More Medicaid Spending Improve the Economy?
*February 4, 2015*

Proponents of putting more people on Medicaid, the federal program for the poor, say the increased government spending will improve the economy. Is this true?

Medicaid is a health care entitlement that began in 1965. Originally, it provided health insurance to low-income families with children. It has grown to include aid for disability and long-term care. The existing Medicaid costs are covered with both federal and state taxpayer dollars on a 50/50 basis.

One of the main goals of the Affordable Care Act (ACA), or Obamacare, is to expand Medicaid to all low-income adults. The federal government enticed states to expand the program by paying 100 percent of the costs for the first three years and then gradually dropping the federal contribution to 90 percent. To date, 26 states, including Washington state, have accepted the offer electing to expand their Medicaid populations.

The Washington State Legislature never voted directly on accepting Medicaid expansion, instead rolling the federal money into the 2013–2015 budget.

The Medicaid program has many problems. Tragically, multiple studies show that health outcomes for Medicaid patients are no better than for people with no health insurance. Although the cost of Medicaid to taxpayers has exploded, payments to doctors are very low—in many cases only 40 percent of what private insurance pays. Consequently, fewer doctors can afford to see Medicaid patients and still pay their office overhead. Finding a doctor is a significant problem for Medicaid patients.

In spite of these problems, proponents of Obamacare strongly favor expanding the program. Their latest argument is that Medicaid spending provides economic benefits to the entire state. Washington State's Office of Financial Management calculates Medicaid expansion provided an additional $1.21 billion last year. The reasoning here is that more Medicaid spending adds new health care jobs and more wages. Those dollars then trickle down to the general economy.

The argument might make sense until you realize that entitlement spending is only half the story. Entitlement dollars must come from taxes, which are taken from other consumer spending. The studies that show an economic benefit from Medicaid neglect to account for other uses of those tax dollars. In other words, if the money wasn't paying for Medicaid, it would go to other economic activities. There might be fewer jobs in health care, but there would be more jobs in other areas of the economy.

It's like bailing water out of the deep end of a swimming pool and pouring it into the shallow end while expecting the whole pool to get larger in the process.

Entitlements do not create wealth. Health economist Dr. Robert A. Book researched the impact of Medicaid expansion and included the dead-weight burden of taxes to pay for the entitlement. He found that if all states expanded Medicaid, the economic loss to the country would be $174 billion over ten years, and the job loss would be a net 206,000 jobs lost per year. Washington state would see a loss of $13.5 billion over ten years, with 16,500 jobs lost each year, according to this estimate.

Proponents of Medicaid expansion say Washington state will leave federal dollars "on the table" if we do not expand the program. This argument ignores the fact that state taxpayers are also federal taxpayers. Any expansion of Medicaid is a burden on state taxpayers regardless of which branch of government dispenses the money. Estimates of the total cost to taxpayers for the Medicaid expansion in Washington state alone range from $17 billion to $22 billion over the next ten years.

Instead of forcing low-income people into a poor insurance plan, our elected officials should promote meaningful health insurance choices. Rather than an open-ended entitlement, state officials should strongly lobby the federal government to provide a fixed, block-grant sum of money for our Medicaid patients. The Medicaid budget could then be predictable.

Other states, such as Indiana, have tried innovative health savings accounts and state-funded, high-deductible health insurance plans. These plans allow Medicaid patients to make their own health care decisions and find health care in the private market.

Expanding Medicaid gives more people health insurance on paper. It does not, however, give people better access to good care, and it certainly doesn't improve the overall economy.

# Make Medical Providers Compete on Price
## as Well as Quality
### *February 9, 2015*

The method doctors and hospitals are paid for their work is undergoing gradual but relentless change. Providers traditionally have been compensated on a fee-for-service basis, where they receive a specific amount of money for a specific visit or medical procedure. This is how other highly trained professionals, like lawyers, dentists, auto mechanics, and architects are paid—they receive a fee for service rendered.

The main argument offered against allowing doctors to charge for their services is that it leads to overutilization and increases health care costs. Doctors are accused of ordering more visits, extra tests, and unnecessary operations simply to pad their incomes.

From an economic standpoint, the fundamental difference with health care is the third-party payer system in the United States. The overwhelming majority of health care in this country is paid for by employers or the government, with money channeled through heavily regulated insurance companies. In other economic activities, consumers pay directly for a product or service and consequently become savvy shoppers who can take advantage of marketplace competition. In health care, patients are largely barred from shopping and have become isolated from the true costs they incur.

Third-party payers were disinterested until health care costs and utilization exploded. Now, the payers, and not patients or providers, are attempting to change the payment model by imposing wage and price controls on doctors and hospitals. Patients are not seeking these caps, they are cost-control efforts by the entities that have to pay the bills.

A second argument against doctor fees is it discourages the use of "integrated care," by which patients are placed in some type of provider group that controls all aspects of their care. These integrated groups have many different names, including medical homes and accountable care organizations. In reality, they are simply various forms of the health maintenance organizations (HMOs).

HMOs may or may not provide integrated care but, through force, they can hold down health care costs. HMOs decrease health care costs by using a gatekeeper system where clinical decisions are weighed against budgets. Various types of HMOs are strongly encouraged or outright mandated in the Affordable Care Act.

The idea of pay-for-performance is becoming popular with payers, regulators, and policymakers. The reason is that they, not patients or doctors, decide what "performance" means and how much the "pay" will be. Providers get paid a higher amount if they meet certain quality measures that are determined, in many cases, by non-clinician policymakers or other regulators.

Results with the pay-for-performance model over the past 15 years have varied. There is no clear evidence its defined quality measures decrease patient complications, improve care or predictably lower costs. It does increase the regulatory and compliance burden on providers, however. In reality, most hospitals have been improving quality measures and the patient experience without pay for performance.

What is a real and meaningful solution to the provider reimbursement problem?

First, solve the third-party payer problem by removing employers and the government as payers of most health care. Allow patients, working with their providers, to make their own medical decisions and control their own health care dollars. Change the tax code and allow individuals to take the same health insurance deduction employers now receive. Use government programs such as Medicare and Medicaid as safety-net plans for low-income people. Reform or repeal the vast new system of government controls imposed by the Affordable Care Act.

Second, allow more competition in the health insurance industry by eliminating many of the government benefit mandates. Let patients decide what insurance plans are best for them and allow them to purchase plans across state lines. Encourage the use of health savings accounts and low-cost, high-deductible insurance plans.

Third, increase the use of high-risk pools for high-use and high-cost patients.

Fourth, pass meaningful tort reform so providers don't feel the need to order extra tests out of fear of lawsuits.

Finally, encourage more price transparency in the system and allow providers to compete on price as well as quality, just as professionals do in other parts of our economy.

The most important person in the healthncare system is the patient, not cost-conscious employers or distant government bureaucrats. The patient, as a consumer of health care, should determine the value and quality of services received and how much doctors should be paid to provide them.

## Medicare and Medicaid at 50—
## Decades of Increasing Costs and Diminishing Services
## Reveal the Problems of Socialized Medicine
*August 24, 2015*

Medicare and Medicaid were enacted in 1965 as part of President Lyndon Johnson's ambitious Great Society effort to end poverty. The original programs were designed to provide health insurance for all seniors 65 and older and for children of low-income families. Although opponents warned the programs were the first steps to socialized medicine, the law was supported by Democrats and Republicans.

Today, almost 30 percent of Americans are enrolled in these two programs. In Washington state, some 1.13 million people are in Medicare, and 1.8 million are in Medicaid. This means over 40 percent of the state's population has health insurance paid for by taxpayers.

As an enticement or coercion, Medicare is tied to Social Security (SS) benefits. If seniors try to opt out of Medicare, they lose their Social Security benefits. Medicare is funded by an ever increasing payroll tax and by an ever increasing percent of the federal general tax fund. As more money comes from the general fund, Medicare becomes a pay-as-you-go plan and moves closer to a pure entitlement, not "socialized insurance" as originally envisioned. Likewise, the number of workers per enrollee has decreased substantially since 1965.

Medicare is a single-payer, government-controlled socialized health care plan. By 1970, the private health insurance market for seniors, except to cover copays, had collapsed. The private sector quickly found that it is impossible to compete with a government monopoly.

Financing is a persistent problem for Medicare. By 1990, the program was nine times over the original budget. In 1974, it consumed less than one percent of the economy, but it gradually increased to 3.5 percent last year. The Medicare trustees now report the trust fund, or financial reserve, will run out by 2030.

The Affordable Care Act (ACA), or Obamacare, compounds

Medicare funding problems. A large part of the payment for the ACA comes from cuts to Medicare. To control future utilization in Medicare, the ACA directs officials to establish a non-elected committee, the Independent Payment Advisory Board, to determine "best practices" for providers. The IPAB theoretically cannot ban services because of cost, but for the panel to be effective in controlling costs and the prices of tests and treatments will have to be considered.

Medicaid began as a pure entitlement with funding from both federal and state taxpayers. The cost and enrollment in Medicaid have exploded, and it is now one of the largest budget items for every state.

The ACA extended Medicaid to all low-income adults, although the U.S. Supreme Court ruled states could choose not to expand their programs. A majority have expanded Medicaid because the federal government will initially pay 100 percent, and ultimately 90 percent, of the new costs. Of course, federal taxpayers are also state taxpayers, so this is not "free" money.

Doctor payments in Medicaid are only 40 to 50 percent of what private insurance pays. Consequently, providers lose money for every entitlement patient they treat and are forced to limit the number of Medicaid patients they see. A recent Kaiser survey found that 37 percent of Medicaid patients had difficulty finding a doctor.

The real tragedy is that having Medicaid insurance results in no better health outcomes than being uninsured. A recent Harvard University study confirmed this fact and also found that people with Medicaid go to the emergency room more often than people with no insurance.

We now have 50 years of experience with two socialized medicine programs in the U.S. There is no question they have helped millions of people, but it is unlikely they are better than affordable market-based alternatives that were blocked when these government-centered programs passed.

There also is widespread agreement they are not sustainable in their present forms. More government intervention can control costs, but only through rationing of health care. To increase choice, maintain or improve quality and control costs, seniors and low-income patients should be allowed to control their own health care dollars and make their own health care decisions.

## Making Dollars and Sense Out of Drug Prices
### October 21, 2015

Presidential candidates Hillary Clinton and Bernie Sanders, as well as many other elected officials, are demanding that the government impose price controls on medicines as a way to bring down health care costs. In 2013, prescription drug costs accounted for just nine percent of overall health care expenses. In economics, setting price limits on goods and services always results in scarcity, with fewer of those things being produced and made available to consumers. This has been confirmed by the disastrous centrally planned economies of communist countries.

There is a great deal of confusion and misunderstanding about drug pricing, manufacturing, marketing, and the impact of government regulations in the United States. This confusion has only been made worse by the recent egregious behavior of Turing Pharmaceuticals, which raised the price of Daraprim, a drug that fights parasitic infections, by 4,100 percent.

Only five percent of drugs make it through clinical trials and go on to be marketed and make money for their manufacturers. Over 95 percent of research on new drugs loses money and fails to produce treatments. The final pricing of the successful drug must make up for all the money spent on the research and development (R&D) of all the previous failures.

On average, the ten largest drug manufacturers spend 16 percent of their total revenue on R&D. A better comparison across industries is the percent of sales spent on R&D. According to the National Science Foundation, in 2013, the average of sales profit across all industries spent on R&D was 3.3 percent. The pharmaceutical industry spent 10.3 percent of total sales profit on R&D, about the same as the computer and electronic industry, which was 10.6 percent.

Drug companies are heavily criticized for their large advertizing budgets. However, research shows that there is a substantial range for what pharmaceutical manufactures spend on marketing. According to the BBC News, in 2013, the ten largest drug companies spent between 17.9 percent and 28.4 percent of total revenue on advertizing. The average was 23 percent. Compare that to the 21 to 23 percent that IBM and Microsoft spend on marketing.

Just as professional athletes command large salaries because of their time-limited careers, innovative drug manufacturers have a limited amount of time to earn a profit on a drug before the patent expires. Once a drug goes "off patent," it must compete with generic drugs. Generic manufacturers have a definite role in the health care system and can offer good prices, but they don't have the added expense of R&D.

Government price controls not only limit the supply of a product, they also limit the interest of financial investors in a company. Seattle biopharmaceutical companies experienced this recently when their stock prices dropped 13 percent in one week (falling six percent in one day!) simply because of Secretary Clinton's price-control announcement. Fewer investors mean less money for life-saving new drugs and less competition in developing those drugs.

The high prices of new pharmaceuticals must also be weighed in comparison to the cost of treating a patient without that drug. For example, Sovaldi is a drug that treats hepatitis C and costs $84,000 for a curative three-month treatment. The alternative, a liver transplant, costs over $300,000 and is associated with a great deal of pain and suffering, assuming a donor liver is even available.

If politicians really want to bring prices down and increase competition in the drug industry, they should focus on streamlining the drug approval process to decrease the time and money manufacturers spend on bringing a new drug to market. Depending on the study, the average cost of bringing a drug to market today is $2.5 to $5 billion and takes ten to 15 years to get through the government regulatory process.

Putting price controls on drugs will not solve the fundamental problem of our health care delivery system. Unlike the electronics or computer markets, in health care, a third party, either the government through Medicare, Medicaid, and Obamacare, or employers through insurance companies, pays for the majority of health care in the United States.

Throughout our economy, the free market, without third-party interference, results in better products at cheaper prices. Allowing patients, in consultation with their providers, to decide which drugs are best clinically and financially for them should be the goal of health care reform, not damaging price controls.

## Cost of Medicaid Entitlement has Crowded Out
## State Money for Higher Education
*January 6, 2016*

During the 2015 legislative session, the legislature lowered tuition at Washington state colleges and universities. The policy shift, while welcome, does not solve the funding crowd-out problem created by the state Medicaid program.

The Washington state budget has increased more than 400 percent in inflation-adjusted dollars since Medicaid was enacted in 1965. Taxes today are higher than ever, while the state population has little more than doubled. Over the past 50 years, fast-growing spending on the Medicaid entitlement has crowded out funding for other core responsibilities of the state government.

Congress enacted the traditional Medicaid entitlement program in 1965. From the beginning, the program was funded by the federal government matching state spending with a 50/50 contribution. Of course, federal and state taxpayers are the same people, so for taxpayers, the "match" is meaningless.

The Affordable Care Act, or Obamacare, expands Medicaid to any low-income adult 18 years of age and older. Federal taxpayers fund the majority of the expanded Medicaid until 2020, and then state taxpayers pay ten percent.

In 2014 inflation-adjusted dollars, the Washington state budget was $3.7 billion in 1964, with no funds allocated to Medicaid. At that time, higher education in Washington state received 14 percent of the state budget.

The state budget grew 300 percent to $11.6 billion by 1990. Medicaid spending accounted for 24 percent of the budget, and the portion of the state budget for higher education dropped to 12 percent.

Medicaid spending accounted for 27 percent of the budget in 2013, and the level of state funding for higher education fell to nine percent.

Over the years, the tuition charged by the University of Washington has relentlessly increased. In 2014 inflation-adjusted dollars, tuition was $2,500 per year in 1965, increased to $3,500 in 1990 and had nearly quadrupled to $12,000 per year by 2014.

Tuition paid by students covers only part of the total cost of education. The total cost of educating one student in Washington state universities, however, has remained remarkably stable.

In 1990, Washington state taxpayers paid 84 percent of the full cost of education and the students, through tuition, paid 16 percent. By 2014, however, the state's contribution had dropped to 34 percent, and students paid 66 percent of the cost, even though the number of students enrolled had been relatively constant.

State officials are elected to make decisions about the priorities of government and the overall size and cost of government. Over the past 50 years, federal and state officials have chosen to expand the Medicaid entitlement and place a greater financial burden on taxpayers. State officials have also required students to pay more for their college education.

In addition to crowding out funding for higher education, the growing Medicaid entitlement program has resulted in a number of other harmful consequences. First, it discourages work and job training for low-paid employees, since with increasing income, workers face loss of their Medicaid benefits. It also encourages low-wage paying employers not to offer health benefits. They assume, or hope, taxpayers will provide those benefits.

A recent study from researchers at Harvard University published in the *New England Journal of Medicine* found that the real tragedy for people in Medicaid is the program actually provides no better medical outcomes than having no insurance.

State lawmakers unfortunately have been caught in a vicious cycle in which the more they spend on the traditional Medicaid program, the more money they receive from the federal government because of the pre-Obamacare 50/50 funding match. To state officials, federal money feels like it's free. This has increased Medicaid spending at the expense of other state programs like higher education.

A good education is the best way for people to rise out of poverty and make the most of their potential. Last year, the Federal Reserve determined that, on average, a college graduate earns $830,000 more than a high school graduate over a working career.

The goal of elected officials should be to help lift people out of poverty and make them independent and self-sufficient citizens. Making it financially easier for low-income individuals to get an advanced education should be a priority for elected officials rather than trapping them in the welfare Medicaid entitlement.

Washington state lawmakers have an obligation to students, low-income people, and taxpayers to explain honestly why they believe directing more funding to the Medicaid entitlement program is more important than funding higher education for students and their families.

## The Role of Government in Fixing the
## Broken Mental-health System
*August 24, 2016*

The treatment of mentally ill patients has undergone radical changes in the past 150 years, and not always for the better. Care is fragmented and places a huge social burden on American communities. Unfortunately, public-health treatment remains grossly underfunded. But that hopefully is about to change.

The U.S. House recently passed H.R. 2646 to make the federal government accountable, on an outcomes basis, for the $130 billion spent annually on mental-health treatment. Multiple mental-health organizations and media outlets, including *The Seattle Times*, support the bill, called the Helping Families in Mental Health Crisis Act.

The U.S. Senate is expected to pass similar legislation. Gov. Jay Inslee and King County Executive Dow Constantine, taking the recommendations from a dedicated task force, are now making mental-health treatment a priority.

People with mental illnesses range from well-functioning individuals to those with severe disabilities. The role of government is to serve as a safety net and to help dysfunctional, impaired people who may do harm to themselves or others.

Institutionalizing the mentally ill became popular in the mid-nineteenth century, and the federal government funded psychiatric hospitals, or asylums. Community and home-based treatment began in the 1950s and was placed into federal law in 1963 with the Community Mental Health Centers Construction Act.

Federal action caused existing psychiatric hospitals to rapidly close. From 1955 to 1995, the number of institutionalized patients dropped by 90 percent, and many of these mentally-ill people became homeless. From 1955 to 2000, state psychiatric beds per 100,000 people plummeted from 339 to 22. There is now a shortage of available psychiatric beds both nationally and in Washington state.

Community-based treatment over the past 60 years has included regional mental-health centers, supervised residential homes, psychiatric teams, and improved medications. Research shows that both institutionalization and community treatment can be effective, depending on the patient's specific needs. Both approaches have supporters among mental-health professionals.

The tragedy is that both treatment methods are underfunded by federal, state, and county governments. Just like basic services, such as police, fire, and emergency, the fundamental role of government here is the treatment and protection of the mentally ill. Unlike other areas of health care where patients can make rational choices and direct their own care, providing quality mental treatments for those with no other option is a public-health issue and should be a government priority.

Estimates show that 20 to 30 percent of the Washington state prison population today suffers from significant mental illnesses. This compares to just six percent reported nationally in 1980. County jails in Washington are experiencing an alarming increase in prisoners with psychiatric problems. Some are drug related, but for most of these people, drug abuse is often just one part of a larger mental illness. Studies confirm that 40 percent of patients with severe psychiatric problems have been incarcerated at some point in their lives.

In 2015, a federal judge ruled that prisoners in Washington state must have a competency evaluation within seven days of incarceration. Many patients had been waiting weeks, or even months, in jail before receiving a professional mental examination, let alone caring and constructive treatment for their conditions.

Unfortunately, in July 2016, fewer than one-third of prisoners ordered to receive evaluations and possible treatments were given them within seven days. The judge is currently holding the state Department of Social and Health Services in contempt for not complying with the 2015 ruling. The agency (in other words, the state taxpayers) is now required to pay $500 to $1,000 per day per patient not evaluated within one week.

There has been a tragic and growing trend in the use of regular hospital emergency rooms for "psychiatric boarding" or "warehousing." This is not only costly but, more importantly, can exacerbate the patient's mental problem.

In 2014, the Washington state Supreme Court ruled that emergency-room boarding is illegal. Because of the psychiatric-bed shortage in the state, many mentally ill people wind up back on the streets, living homeless and abandoned. This is one reason that simply building more subsidized housing does not solve one of the root causes of homelessness.

Both Washington state and the federal government currently are placing a huge financial burden on regular hospitals, county and city jails, and state prisons by not allocating sufficient resources to caring for the mentally ill.

The fact that elected officials now recognize the underfunding issue is a promising start to effectively treating mental illnesses. This is good public policy and will immediately make our communities safer. It will help reverse the mistakes of the past and benefit the state prison system, hospitals and, most importantly, people living with mental illnesses.

## Rise in Entitlement-funded Health Care Jobs
## Masks Drop in Private Sector Employment
*August 31, 2016*

The Bureau of Labor Statistics recently released the latest employment numbers. The report tells us that only 38,000 new jobs were created in May, the worst monthly jobs report since 2010.

Analysis of weakness in the various job sectors is very revealing. The health care sector reported 46,000 new jobs. In other words, the non-health care areas actually lost 8,000 jobs.

For the past year, health care employment has increased at almost twice the rate of non-health care employment. From May 2015 to May 2016, total non-farm jobs increased by 2.4 million, or 1.69 percent. For the same time period, health care sector jobs increased by 487,000, or 3.24 percent.

Undoubtedly, the increase in health care sector employment reflects the fact that more people are now insured through the Obamacare exchanges, the Medicaid entitlement has expanded because of Obamacare, and as seniors retire, the Medicare program has increased enrollment. These are government programs paid for by taxpayers. New health care employees do not always work directly for the government, but the vast majority of payments for these programs come directly from taxpayers through the government.

The increase in health care sector employment essentially means more government-funded jobs. The numbers may show growth, but these in no way indicate growth in the private wealth-generating economy. Only in the private sector can overall productivity increase. Expanding government does nothing to increase the size of a country's economy. It is like bailing water out of the deep end of a swimming pool and pouring it into the shallow end while expecting the whole pool to get larger in the process.

Research done by the Georgetown University Center on Education and Workforce shows that the majority of these new health care sector jobs are in low-paying work areas such as nurse aides. These are important jobs, but without substantially more education, these workers find themselves in terminal positions with little opportunity for advancement. The country is not adding significantly more registered nurses and doctors.

Proponents of government programs say expanding entitlements grows the economy, not realizing that all public money has to be taken out of the private sector first. It is unclear how increasing taxes or borrowing against future generations increases the financial well-being for states and the nation.

The argument might sound good until you realize that entitlement spending is only half the story. Entitlement dollars must come from taxes, which are taken from other consumer spending. The studies that show an economic benefit from a government program neglect to account for the lost uses of those tax dollars. In other words, if the money were not paying for an entitlement, it would go to other productive economic activities. There might be fewer jobs in health care, but there would be more jobs in other areas of the economy.

Entitlements do not create wealth, for they only involve government power inefficiently moving money from one place to another. Health economist Dr. Robert A. Book researched the impact of Medicaid expansion and included the dead-weight burden of taxes to pay for the entitlement. He found that if all states expanded Medicaid, the economic loss to the country would be $174 billion over ten years. Because Washington state officials elected to expand Medicaid, the state will potentially see an economic loss of $13.5 billion over ten years due to other lost productive activities.

The national economy has struggled to recover from the Great Recession of 2008. The middle socioeconomic class continues to shrink. Adding a higher percentage of government jobs compared to private jobs will never improve the economy and expand the workforce with well-paying employment. Elected officials must reform entitlements, allow more health care choices, decrease the tax load on Americans, especially the middle class, and cut the regulatory burden on employers to truly jump start the economy.

# How Washington Residents Are Hurt by
# the Affordable Care Act
*February 13, 2017*

Congress is currently debating repeal of the Affordable Care Act (ACA), also known as Obamacare, and enacting some form of replacement. Defenders of the ACA argue that even though the law only provided health insurance to 40 percent of the uninsured and that it has not decreased health care costs, it has been an economic boom to the country and to Washington state.

Supporters say Washington state would lose 45,000 jobs and billions of federal taxpayer dollars if the ACA were repealed. The state's Office of Financial Management calculates Medicaid expansion alone provides more than $1 billion per year. The reasoning here is that more Medicaid spending adds new health care jobs and more wages. Those dollars then trickle down to the general economy.

The argument might make sense until you realize that government spending is only half the story. Entitlement dollars must come from taxes, which are taken from other consumer spending. The studies that show an economic benefit from Medicaid neglect to account for other uses of those tax dollars. In other words, if the money wasn't paying for Medicaid, it would go to other economic activities. There might be fewer jobs in health care, but there would be more jobs in other areas of the economy.

Obamacare's defenders argue as if bailing water out of the deep end of a swimming pool and pouring it into the shallow end will make the whole pool larger.

Entitlement spending does not create wealth. Health economist Dr. Robert A. Book researched the impact of Medicaid expansion and included the dead-weight burden of taxes to pay for the entitlement. He found that if all states expanded Medicaid, the economic loss to the country would be $174 billion over ten years, and the job loss would be a net 206,000 jobs lost per year. Washington state would see a loss of $13.5 billion over ten years, with 16,500 jobs lost each year, according to this estimate.

The ACA is financed by only two things: taxes and severe cuts in Medicare. Although there are new taxes on the "rich," there are also taxes on drugs, medical devices, insurance companies, and insurance plans. These taxes are passed on to everyone who uses health care, not just the "rich."

Proponents of the ACA also ignore how their cuts to Medicare hurt seniors' access to health care. Before the passage of the ACA, Medicare paid providers a fraction of what private insurance paid. This limited doctors' ability to treat seniors and still pay their overhead costs. The ACA made this problem worse and reduced access to health care for seniors even further.

Although some hospitals and doctors gained income through the ACA by treating more Medicaid patients, many are facing significant decreases in their reimbursements from Medicare.

Worse, the ACA has done nothing to bring down the cost of health care. Last year, health care accounted for 18 percent of the U.S. economy. This is projected to grow to 20 percent by 2020 if the law is not repealed. Proponents of the ACA falsely claim that central planning through the use of such things as electronic health records and accountable care organizations will bring costs down. There is no evidence these are cost effective or provide better health care outcomes.

ACA defenders make no mention of the series of broken promises they used to get the law passed; premiums would go down, every family would save $2,500 a year, you could keep your doctor, you could keep your health plan. The defenders of Obamacare created this mess, and now they are criticizing the national leaders who are trying to fix it.

More government intervention is not the solution to our health care problem. Meaningful reform that puts patients, not bureaucrats, in charge of their own health care is the real solution. Decreasing costly insurance mandates, greater use of major medical, catastrophic health insurance plans, encouraging the use of health savings accounts, and meaningful reform to the Medicaid and Medicare entitlements offer the best chance for universal coverage and cost-control in our health care system.

# Is Health Care a Right?

*April 8, 2017*

"We hold these truths to be self-evident, that all men are created equal, that they are endowed by their Creator with certain unalienable Rights, that among these are Life, Liberty and the pursuit of Happiness."

These words in the Declaration of Independence define the "rights" of American citizens. They do not include health care. Yet for over 100 years, some Americans have believed that health care is not only a right, but that the government should provide it and taxpayers should pay for it.

If medical treatment is a right, then what exactly does that mean? Does it mean that your neighbors, through the government, are obligated to provide all health care for you? Does it mean that anyone can demand the government to pay for hospitalization, for prescription drugs, and for specialty treatments like organ transplants? Does it mean that every American has a right to the skill and knowledge of all physicians and providers?

These questions lead to other questions. How does society pay for health care for all? Who gets to decide who should receive health care and how much? Who gets to decide what the health care budget should be? Who should have the power to make health care decisions for us?

Or rather than confront these issues, do proponents of health care as a right mean everyone should have health insurance? The problem with this belief is that simply having health insurance does not guarantee timely access to actual medical care. Every citizen of Canada has government-paid health insurance, but the long wait times for treatment, most notably for specialty care, would be unacceptable for Americans.

Everyone can agree that health care is a necessity of life. So are food, shelter, and clothing. Yet no one is demanding universal "food care" or universal government housing. The critical issue is that people expect *access* to food, shelter, and clothing. Americans expect choices and competition when they shop for these necessities of life.

The government exists to guarantee free markets for Americans when they seek access to virtually any product, but especially access to food, shelter, and clothing. No one would expect society, through government, to pay for these necessities of life for everyone.

If "food care" was controlled, paid for, and regulated by the government, we would have overutilization, fewer choices, and a limited supply. The private system of grocery stores and supermarkets guarantees access, choice, and competitive prices for everyone. The free-market system is efficient, voluntary, and fair.

The critical point is utilizing the best mechanism to allow the greatest number of Americans access to health care. The Canadian single-payer system does not guarantee timely access. The American experience with the Veterans Administration hospital system, a comprehensive government-controlled, single-payer health care program, reveals unacceptable wait times and huge inefficiencies. Fundamentally, these systems ration health care by waiting lists and limited money. The quality of care can be variable.

Because of budgetary constraints, the demand for health care is much greater than the supply in virtually every country with a government-controlled health care system. Even Medicare, essentially a single-payer plan, is not financially sustainable.

Just like in all other economic activities, the free market offers the best solution to provide the greatest access to health care and to control costs. People freely making their own health care decisions and using their own health care dollars would give Americans the best chance to utilize their "right" to access health care, with safety-net health programs provided for those who can't afford it.

At the end of the day, health care is an economic activity like any other, albeit with the most personal of interactions between patient and provider. Society should work towards putting patients in charge of their health care, reducing the role of government, and focusing on access, not health care as a supposed "right."

## Insurance Coverage May Not Ensure Better Health
*September 10, 2017*

The nation continues to debate health care reform. The Affordable Care Act, or Obamacare, has provided health insurance for 20 million Americans, half of whom were placed in the expanded Medicaid entitlement. Yet the ACA has not accomplished its goals of providing universal health insurance and controlling the ever-rising cost of health care.

However, ACA supporters continue to argue that having health insurance saves lives. Former Senate Majority Leader Harry Reid, D-Nevada, said in 2009 that 45,000 Americans die each year because they don't have health insurance. Sen. Bernie Sanders, I-Vermont, argues that 36,000 people will die each year if Obamacare is repealed. Other advocates are less specific but claim that Americans will become "sick" again if the ACA is overturned.

Unquestionably, some people have been helped by being newly insured. However, simply having health insurance does not guarantee timely access to medical treatment, while not having insurance does not predictably influence mortality rates.

Multiple studies have tried to show a relationship between higher mortality rates and being uninsured. One of the most famous was published by the Institute of Medicine in 2002 and concluded that being uninsured caused a 25 percent higher death rate than being insured. Subsequent research of the same patient group revealed that a respondent's health status, such as obesity and health behavior, such as smoking, fully accounted for the difference in mortality rates. Researchers found that insurance status had nothing to do with a person's risk of dying.

A second often-quoted study came from Harvard University. It looked at mortality rates in three states that expanded Medicaid in the early 2000s. Only New York had a significant decrease in mortality, whereas Arizona and Maine saw no difference between insured and uninsured populations. The study was essentially inconclusive.

At least half of the newly insured under the ACA nationally and 80 percent in Washington state were placed in the Medicaid entitlement. It is now well known that having Medicaid health insurance is no better for a person's health outcomes than being uninsured.

In 2008, Oregon lawmakers decided they had enough additional public money to put more people into the state's Medicaid program. Oregon officials held a lottery that ultimately signed up 6,400 new Medicaid enrollees. A further 5,800 people were eligible for the program but were not selected. People in this group had the same health and economic profile as the lottery winners, allowing researchers to make valid comparisons. This created the perfect test-case on the effectiveness of Medicaid in providing care. These 5,800 people became the control group in an objective, randomized health care study.

*The New England Journal of Medicine* reported the results. The conclusion is revealing. It turns out that being put on Medicaid did not improve health outcomes nor improve mortality statistics compared to having no insurance coverage at all. The Medicaid group had no improvement in the important objective health measurements of blood sugar levels, blood pressure, and cholesterol levels. Abnormal levels of these parameters are definite precursors to cardiovascular disease, the most common killer in the U.S.

The insurance benefits in the ACA began in 2014. The mortality rate in the U.S. has actually gone up in the past two years. In 2015, states that expanded Medicaid under the ACA saw an increase in mortality of nine deaths per 100,000. States that did not expand Medicaid experienced an increase in mortality of six deaths per 100,000. This is not a significant difference, but it does show that gaining Medicaid coverage had no effect on mortality.

The data is now very clear that having health insurance is not the same as obtaining timely access to medical care and to a decrease in mortality rates. The goal of health care reform should not simply be to give people insurance cards. Instead, reform should allow patients, as consumers of health care, the best opportunity to acquire the care they want and need. This will have a real impact on mortality rates.

## Single-payer Would Devastate the Economy
### December 7, 2017

Health care reform has once again taken center stage in U.S. domestic policy debates. Progressives continue to promote the single-payer idea, with former presidential candidate, Senator Bernie Sanders and others, advocating for "Medicare for All."

The Affordable Care Act (ACA), also known as Obamacare, is a highly complex law and has made our current health care system more confusing. A single-payer system is attractive to many people because of its perceived simplicity—the U.S. government would provide direct health services to all Americans.

We already have two examples of a single-payer system in the U.S. The Veterans Administration (VA) health care system is a pure socialized, single-payer program. Taxpayers fund the system, the hospitals are owned by the government, and the providers are all government employees. Although the VA system has offered good health care to many of our veterans, we have learned recently that on balance the system is plagued with cost overruns, inefficiencies, and prolonged wait times for care.

The second example is Medicare, which began in 1965 and is a single-payer system for seniors, 65 years of age and older. Funding is through payroll taxes, premiums, and an ever increasing percentage of money from federal general taxes. By 1990, spending in Medicare was seven times over the original budget. Medicare is not financially sustainable in its present form.

Like the VA system, Medicare has helped many people, but the cost of "Medicare for All" would devastate the overall economy. The non-partisan Committee for a Responsible Federal Budget (CRFB) analyzed Senator Sanders' proposal from a financial standpoint. He calls for six new or expanded taxes. Everyone would pay 6.2 percent more in payroll tax and 2.2 percent more in income tax.

Higher-income workers would experience four additional taxes.

Income taxes would increase, capital gains would be taxed as ordinary income, certain current deductions would be eliminated, and estate taxes would increase.

Even with these expanded taxes, the CRFB reports that multiple analysts, including the non-partisan Congressional Budget Office, find Senator Sanders' calculations to be short by up to $14 trillion over ten years.

Canada has had a single-payer system for over 30 years, and its experience is revealing. Canadians are proud that every citizen has health insurance. From a cultural standpoint, the principle of universal coverage is a priority for the country. It also makes it easier for the citizens to overlook the problems within the system.

The demand for health care far outweighs the supply of care in Canada. Health care spending is now one of the greatest expenses for every province in the country.

The long wait times in Canada are not in the patient's best interest and would not be acceptable for the vast majority of Americans. Health care rationing through waiting lists is effective when supply is overwhelmed by demand. The question is whether government bureaucrats should have the authority to pick and choose what procedures patients receive and who should actually receive those treatments while others are forced to wait for care.

Canada actually has a two-tiered health care system. Wealthy Canadians who do not want to wait for care, and can pay cash, can and do receive treatment in the U.S.

Under a single-payer system, health care spending must compete with all other government activity for funding. This makes health care very political and subject to change with every new budget. It also forces each health care sector, for example hospitals and doctors, to compete with each other for limited money.

A single-payer system sounds like a simple solution to the U.S. health care problem. The reality, however, is far different. Fundamentally, a single-payer system centralizes all health care with the government is far too expensive and limits access to health care by rationing. Instead of patients and doctors making key health care decisions, bureaucrats get to make those life and death choices about the kind and amount of health care people receive.

# Imposing Price Controls on Drugs Would be Harmful to Patients and to Our Health Care System
## December 11, 2017

In spite of the promise that the Affordable Care Act would reverse ever-rising health care costs in the United States, Americans continue to experience higher medical expenses. Many elected officials and concerned citizens are now demanding price controls on drugs as a way to decrease health care costs.

In economics, setting price limits on goods and services always results in scarcity, with fewer of those things being produced and made available to consumers. This has been confirmed by the disastrous centrally planned economies of communist countries. Price controls on drugs would be no different.

The Center for Medicare and Medicaid Services reported that prescription drugs accounted for only ten percent of total health care expenses in 2015. This represented one of the slowest-growing cost items in health care.

Only five percent of drugs make it through clinical trials and go on to make money for their manufacturers. Over 95 percent of research on new drugs loses money and fails to produce treatments. The final pricing of the few successful drugs must make up for all the money spent on the research and development (R&D) of all the previous failures.

The Tufts Center for the Study of Drug Development reported in 2014 that the total research cost for a new cancer drug was $2.6 billion. Various studies find that the timeline from the start of research to clinical approval of a new drug is ten to 15 years.

The U.S. accounts for 40 percent of global pharmaceutical profits and funds the majority of drug research. Most other countries have some form of nationalized health care and impose price controls on drugs. If the U.S. paid the same as other industrialized countries do, a significant number of new life-improving and life-savings drugs would not be developed.

On average, the ten largest drug manufacturers spend 16 percent of their total revenue on research and development. A better comparison across industries is the percent of sales spent on R&D. According to the National Science Foundation, in 2013, the average of sales profit across all industries spent on R&D was 3.3 percent. The pharmaceutical industry spent 10.3 percent of total sales profit on R&D, about the same as the computer and electronic industry, which spent 10.6 percent.

Drug companies are heavily criticized for their large advertizing budgets. However, research shows that there is a substantial range for what pharmaceutical manufactures spend on marketing. In 2013 the ten largest drug companies spent between 17.9 percent and 28.4 percent of total revenue on advertizing. The average was 23 percent. Compare that to the 21 to 23 percent that IBM and Microsoft spend on marketing. These companies in other industries are not being singled out for price controls.

Just as professional athletes command large salaries because of their time-limited careers, innovative drug manufacturers have a limited amount of time to earn a profit on a drug before the patent expires. Once a drug goes "off patent," it must compete with generic drugs. Generic manufacturers have a definite role in the health care system and can offer good prices, but they don't have the added expense of research and development.

The current leadership of the Food and Drug Administration has made the streamlining of the drug approval process a priority. This has the potential to decrease the time and money manufacturers spend on bringing a new drug to market. That's good for patients and good for our health care system.

Putting price controls on drugs will not solve the fundamental problem of our health care delivery system. Unlike the electronics or computer markets, in health care, a third party, either the government through Medicare, Medicaid, and Obamacare, or employers through insurance companies, pays for the majority of health care in the United States.

Throughout our economy, the free market, without third-party interference, results in better products at cheaper prices. Allowing patients, in consultation with their doctors, to decide which drugs are best clinically and financially for them should be the goal of health care reform, not damaging price controls.

## Advocates Want to Impose a Single-payer, Government-run Health Care System—One Step at a Time
*March 31, 2018*

Advocates for socialized medicine in the United States have actively campaigned for a government-run system since the beginning of the twentieth century. Theodore Roosevelt ran for president on a platform that included universal health care. Franklin Roosevelt included government-run medicine in his New Deal social program, but he withdrew it because it was unpopular and jeopardized the passage of his Social Security bill.

Complete socialization of the U.S. health care system has never enjoyed the support of the American public. After World War II, many advocates abandoned the goal of a complete government takeover of health care and instead focused on an incremental approach to achieve a single-payer system. Senator Ted Kennedy was one of the leading voices for this gradual movement toward imposing a single-payer system.

In 1965, President Johnson and Congress passed the Medicare and Medicaid entitlement programs. Medicare is a single-payer system for seniors. People 65 years of age and older now have no other choice for major medical health insurance. Medicaid is a pure welfare entitlement for low-income people, paid for by state and federal taxpayers.

The Affordable Care Act (or Obamacare) further entrenched government control over the U.S. health care system by expanding the Medicaid entitlement and by giving taxpayer subsidies to individuals to purchase health insurance in government-mandated exchanges. The ACA did not deliver "health care for all" as advocates promised, but it did add an additional 20 million people to government health care.

There are currently 140 million Americans, or 43 percent of the population, in one of the government-run, taxpayer-funded health care plans. These include Medicare, Medicaid, Obamacare, and the Veterans Administration.

Senator Bernie Sanders (I-VT) ran for president in 2016 on a platform that included universal, government-run health care. He introduced his "Medicare for All" idea as a Senate bill in 2017, with 16 co-sponsors. Rep. John Conyers (D-MI) has for many years submitted a single-payer bill in the U.S. House. His most recent in 2017 had 120 co-sponsors.

Along with these single-payer bills, many of these co-sponsors have recently authored bills in both the Senate and House that would bolster and expand existing government health care programs—again, an incremental approach to the goal of imposing socialized medicine on everyone.

All of these single-payer plans have two fundamental problems: government control of our health care system with the accompanying rationing of medical treatments and the cost.

A single-payer system centralizes all health care with the government. Bureaucrats, not patients and their providers, get to make life and death decisions about the kind and amount of health care people receive.

The non-partisan Committee for a Responsible Federal Budget analyzed Senator Sanders' proposal from a financial standpoint. He calls for six new or expanded taxes. Even with these expanded taxes, the CRFB reports that multiple analysts, including the non-partisan Congressional Budget Office, find Senator Sanders' calculations to be short of the funding needed by up to $14 trillion over ten years.

Although the tax increases would be staggering, the overall impact on the U.S. economy and economic growth would be devastating. There are now multiple examples of countries that enacted socialist programs and ultimately mired their citizens in stagnant economies and lower standards of living.

The Medicare program, created in 1965, was seven times over the original budget estimate by 1990. There is no reason to believe a huge government entitlement like "Medicare for All" or any single-payer system would remain under its proposed budget.

Half of all Americans receive their health insurance from their employer or their spouse's employer. A single-payer system would eliminate employer-paid health insurance and force all of these workers into the government-run plan.

Recent polls show that health care remains an important issue for American families. The 2018 and 2020 elections will be defining moments in the direction of our health care delivery system. The choice will be more incremental government, bureaucratic intervention with the goal of imposing socialized health care on everyone, or forward-looking market reforms that put patients and doctors in control of their own health care decisions.

## We Need a New Approach to Tackling
## the Opioid Overdose Crisis
*July 3, 2018*

Over the past few years, the number of deaths in the United States related to opioid abuse has increased dramatically. Yet for decades the government has been ineffective at solving the illegal drug problem.

In 1969, President Richard Nixon declared that drug abuse was "a serious national threat." He followed this in 1971 with the statement that drug abuse was "public enemy number one" and announced a "war on drugs." This has been an ongoing battle for 50 years. In spite of the billions of taxpayer dollars spent over the years, the current opioid crisis is a direct result of the failure of this effort.

Any market transaction depends on the supply of a product or service and the demand for that product or service. The illegal drug trade is no different. For a war on drugs to be successful, it must reduce both the supply and the demand for drugs.

The emphasis for the past 50 years in the U.S. has been to combat the supply of drugs and punish those who use drugs illegally. This has cost American taxpayers billions of dollars; however, the current opioid crisis shows the limitations of this approach. As one supply chain is stopped, another takes its place. As one drug becomes less accessible, another takes it place.

According to the federal Center for Disease Control and Prevention (CDC), from 2006 to 2010, the opioid overdose rate tracked closely with the overdose rate of prescription opioid drug users, one per 13,000 prescriptions. From 2010 to 2016, however, the prescription drug death rate dropped while non-medical drug users turned to the use of fentanyl and heroin in the illicit market.

This data strongly suggests that the current opioid crisis is not caused by legal prescription drugs, by medical manufacturers and distributers, or by doctors. Instead, the crisis is caused primarily by abuse of illegal fentanyl, heroin, and to a lesser extent, cocaine. From the CDC's 2016 data, prescription drugs were the cause of just 23 percent of drug-related deaths. While a problem in itself, this is a clear minority compared to illicit drug deaths. Legal prescription drugs are not the cause of today's opioid crisis.

Many who view drug abuse as a disease would like to see the decriminalization of the drug user and more emphasis on prosecuting major suppliers and manufacturers of illegal drugs. This is not to be confused with the legalization of all drugs. Incarceration of the user is extremely expensive for taxpayers and provides no real treatment or long-term solution. Shifting resources to prosecuting suppliers while providing effective treatment for users is not an argument for legalization.

An unintended consequence of the current opioid crisis is that patients who are truly in pain are often denied or limited in the amount of prescription pain-relieving medication they can actually receive. This limitation is obviously a disservice to thousands of patients in pain who could benefit from opioid medications and whose prescribed use of pain medication is not contributing at all to the broader opioid crisis.

It is difficult to show a correlation between legally written prescription drugs and opioid deaths. While the number of opioid overdose deaths has risen over the past ten years, according to the American Medical Association 2018 Task Force, the number of legal drug prescriptions written by doctors decreased 22 percent from 2013 to 2017. From 2016 to 2017 alone, the number of written prescriptions decreased by nine percent.

Elected officials have been unable to close the market for illegal drugs and slow or stop the overdose death rate. Perhaps it is time for a new approach to the drug abuse problem—one that views the drug user as an individual with a preventable and treatable disease, while making every effort to fully prosecute illicit drug manufactures and smugglers.

## So You Say You Want a Single-payer System? Then Get Ready to Wait for Rationed Health Care.
### *January 19, 2019*

As the debate over health care reform rages on, more Americans are thinking we should adopt a single-payer health care system. Virtually all national and state Democratic candidates and elected officials are either advocating for a complete government-run plan or an incremental movement toward a government-managed, single-payer system.

The Fraser Institute is a well-respected think tank in Vancouver, British Columbia. The organization has tracked waiting times for patients to receive health care in Canada for the past 20 years. It surveys specialist physicians across 12 specialties throughout Canada. The institute recently released the waiting list data for 2018.

The median time for specialty treatment once a patient was referred by a primary care doctor was 20 weeks. The low was 15 weeks in Saskatchewan, with a high of 45 weeks in New Brunswick. On average, patients waited nine weeks to see a specialist, then waited an additional 11 weeks to receive treatment. Only 12 percent of delays in treatment were at the patient's request.

There were also delays in diagnostic procedures. In 2018, Canadians waited four weeks to receive a CT scan or an ultra sound and ten weeks to receive an MRI.

The Canadian federal government passed the Canadian Health Care Act in 1984. It is a pure single-payer system. Every Canadian is covered by the plan and, in theory, has access to medical care. The provinces administer the plan with funding from federal taxpayers. The government determines what procedures are medically necessary based on data and statistics.

The supply of health care is overwhelmed by the demand in Canada, leading to severe shortages. Consequently, medical care is rationed using long waiting lists and by limiting the number of certain medical procedures allowed. Costs and waiting times have not improved since 1984.

Long waiting times are more than an inconvenience for Canadians. Simple medical problems, if not treated early, can turn into chronic or life-threatening conditions. Waiting times at the very least prolong pain and suffering for patients. In Canada, health care costs have skyrocketed and now represent the largest expense for every province's budget.

Almost 90 percent of Canadians live within driving distance of the United States. For those Canadians who can afford it and do not want to wait, quality health care is immediately available in the U.S. In reality, Canada has a two-tiered health care system, with the U.S. providing timely care for those willing and able to travel and pay more.

Canada has 40 years experience with single-payer health care. Although most Canadians say they like their system, their culture is different than that in the U.S. Waiting times of 20 weeks for treatment would not be acceptable to the overwhelming majority of Americans.

In addition to long waiting times, a single-payer system discourages innovation. There is virtually no money in the system to encourage investment in new life-saving medicines and medical devices. Lack of innovation guarantees that no new treatments will be discovered, with no improvement in quality of life or life expectancy.

Under a single-payer system, health care spending must compete with all other government activities, such as defense, education, and transportation. This makes health care very political and subject to change with every new budget. It also forces each health care sector, for example hospitals and doctors, to compete with each other for limited government money.

Sure, a single-payer system can "insure" everyone, but it in no way guarantees timely access to medical care. Americans should remember this point and take the Canadian experience seriously. Given what we see to the north, we should reject a complete government-run system. Instead, we should call on elected officials to reform health care so that patients are in charge, not bureaucrats.

## Medicare's Current Bleak Financial Outlook
*April 29, 2019*

The Medicare program's trustees recently released their annual financial report. The report is similar to last year's, and like last year, it again serves as a serious wake-up that the finances for the program are not going in a sustainable direction. The growth of health care spending in general far outpaces inflation and economic growth in the U.S.

In 2018, Medicare's costs consumed 3.7 percent of the country's gross domestic product (GDP). The trustees project this number to increase to 5.9 percent of the economy by 2038. After 2038, spending is estimated to increase to 6.5 percent of GDP. In addition, the Medicare Federal Hospital Insurance Trust Fund, which pays for Medicare Part A hospital care, will run out of money by 2026.

To successfully address the shortfall, Medicare payroll taxes would need to increase by 30 percent, or spending in the program would need to decrease by 20 percent. In other words, workers would see their taxes increase significantly, or hospitals and doctors would experience a dramatic drop in income.

The irony is that, despite looming financial failure, progressives are clamoring that a "Medicare for All," single-payer system be imposed on the entire country. The current Medicare program has an enrollment of 15 percent of the U.S. population. For a single-payer plan to have a chance of surviving, the astronomical increase in taxes would stifle the economy. In addition, provider payments would be so low, and very few talented people would be attracted to the health care field, which would lead to a decrease in quality of care for all patients.

The existing Medicare program is an insurance plan for seniors 65 and older. It is popular with Americans. However, as the trustee report shows, the plan must absolutely be reformed to remain viable. At some point, our elected officials must face reality, not defer to a future Congress, and tackle the runaway spending in Medicare.

A simple first step to Medicare reform would be to gradually raise the age of eligibility. When the program started in 1965, the average life expectancy in the U.S. was 67 years for men and 74 years for women. Average life expectancy is now up to 76 years for men and 81 years for women, straining an entitlement program that was not designed to provide health services to people for so many years late in life.

Another simple Medicare reform would be more thorough means testing. Wealthier seniors would pay more, and low-income people would pay less.

As it stands now, there is, understandably, no private insurance market for seniors. Any private market was crowded out long ago by Medicare. It is virtually impossible to compete with the government, which has monopoly power and an unlimited ability to fix prices and lose money while any potential competitors go out of business.

The private market for the elderly could be resurrected by allowing people to opt out of Medicare voluntarily and allowing those seniors to purchase health savings accounts and high-deductible health plans. Low-income seniors could use vouchers or some type of subsidized premium support that would allow them to purchase health insurance in the private market.

Physicians should be allowed to seek partial payments from patients or their insurance companies, which, by law, they cannot do now unless they leave the Medicare program entirely.

Future generations should be allowed to keep the individual health insurance they want into retirement. That way, as the younger generation saves, their health insurance nest egg would build until they need it in their later years, just as popular IRAs do now.

Solutions do exist that can save the existing Medicare program. Our elected officials will need political courage to implement these measures. Given the program's current problems for patients, taxpayers, and providers, imposing "Medicare for All" on all Americans is not a reasonable or viable solution.

# Washington Legislature Passes a Public Option and Leads the Nation Toward a Single-payer Health Care System
## June 17, 2019

Activists on the political left continue to push the U.S. health care delivery system toward a single-payer, government-controlled plan. Many Americans are now debating a complete nationalized program versus an incremental move to fully socialized medicine. Alternatives such as a Medicare or Medicaid buy-in, dropping the age of eligibility for Medicare, increasing the income threshold for enrollment in Medicaid, and ultimately imposing "Medicare for All" are now actively discussed. These are all potential campaign issues for the 2020 election.

The public option is another incremental move toward adopting a single-payer health care system. The Washington State Legislature passed a public option bill this past session. This is the first in the nation and may serve as a template for other left-leaning states or the federal government.

In the broadest sense, a public option is any government-run health insurance plan that competes against private plans. More specifically, the current terminology refers to a taxpayer-subsidized government plan that would be sold in the Affordable Care Act (ACA) health insurance exchanges. These plans were hotly debated by Congress in 2009 but were left out of the final ACA legislation.

The ACA exchanges are currently in a financial death spiral because of adverse selection. Young, healthy people have opted not to buy heavily regulated and expensive insurance, which leaves older, sicker individuals in the exchanges.

A public option is intended to prop up the exchanges with a plan containing more taxpayer subsidies and more government control. Consequently, over the past few years, the idea has been resurrected both nationally and on a state basis in politically left-leaning states like Washington.

The recently passed legislation establishes a public option in the Washington State Exchange starting in 2021, which will compete against private health insurance plans in the individual market.

These government plans will reduce deductibles, offer more services before deductibles kick in, cap out-of-pocket health care expenses at ten percent of income, maximize subsidies, and limit premium increases. Taxpayer premium subsidies will help out anyone who earns up to 500 percent of the federal poverty level—which in 2019 is $127,000 for a family of four.

The state insurance commissioner will decide what treatments and procedures are included in the public option and whether doctors are providing "quality care." Payments to providers, which are based on Medicare rates, cannot exceed 160 percent of aggregate Medicare payments for like services for any given year and will be reviewed by the commissioner in 2023.

Interestingly enough, the funding mechanism to pay for all of this is not included in the bill. The fiscal note estimates only the administrative costs, but it did not address the huge taxpayer subsidy cost. Either federal taxpayers will be responsible for these, or if denied by federal officials, Washington state taxpayers will see a huge increase in their tax burden.

As the country learned from Medicare, it is impossible for private citizens to compete against the government. The government can use monopolistic practices funded by taxpayers and debt while not needing to earn a profit. There was once a thriving private insurance market for older Americans, but now there is no major medical health insurance alternative for seniors except for Medicare.

The public option, once up and running, will have the same effect on the individual and small-group health insurance markets in Washington state. The impact may very well spill over into the large-group and employer-paid markets.

It is disingenuous for supporters to claim these government plans will increase competition in the exchange. They will devastate the private health insurance markets.

However, one fact is clear. The public option is simply another mechanism for an incremental move to a total nationalized, single-payer health care system for Washington state and potentially the country.

## Health Care Systems in Other Countries—
## Would They Work in the United States?
*August 9, 2019*

The United States has a complex health care delivery system composed of private and government-funded insurance plans. Half of all Americans receive their health insurance from their employer or their spouse's employer. Over 40 percent of Americans receive their health insurance from the government. The remainder are either uninsured or obtain health insurance through the private individual market. The current political debate concerns how large a role the government should play in our health care delivery system.

The United States spends far more money per-person on health care than other industrialized countries. Last year, overall medical spending in the U.S. totaled $3.5 trillion or 18 percent of the national gross domestic product.

Because other countries spend less on health care, they are often used as models for the U.S. However, looking to other countries to solve our health care delivery system problems may not be reasonable. Other countries are smaller than the U.S. and have a more homogenous population. What the people of one country favor may not be applicable or acceptable to people living in a different society.

According to a *Forbes* survey, the U.S. accounts for 38 percent of life-saving and life-extending medical innovations compared to an average of 15 percent in other countries. The U.S. also leads the world in the research and development of pharmaceuticals.

One fact does remain, though. In all other industrialized countries, the demand for health care is much greater than the money budgeted for it. The results of this supply/demand mismatch are chronic shortages followed by strict rationing of health care. The rationing can take many forms—from long waits, to denying the elderly access to certain procedures, to allowing individuals with political influence to receive priority attention from providers.

Canada has a true single-payer, nationalized system that is totally funded by taxpayers. In 2018, wait times for specialty care averaged 20 weeks. In practice, Canada has a two-tiered system in the sense that officials allow their citizens to travel to the U.S. for privately-funded health care.

Great Britain established a comprehensive government health care system in 1948 that gives every citizen cradle-to-grave coverage. About ten percent of the population has private insurance, and many physicians combine government entitlement work with private practice. Over the past year, 250,000 citizens have waited more than six months for planned treatments within the National Health Service, while 36,000 British have waited nine months or more.

Switzerland has a comparatively large private health care sector, and patients are responsible for 30 percent of their own health care costs. Consequently, a certain degree of health care consumerism exists in Switzerland, and the country has been fairly successful in holding down costs. Unfortunately, as officials increase the number of benefit mandates required in insurance plans, health care costs are rising.

Singapore has a multi-tiered system with different levels of care depending on the patient's ability and willingness to pay more. This is similar to the system in the U.S. before the passage of Medicare and Medicaid, when private hospitals and doctors treated paying patients and charity hospitals and residents-in-training cared for low-income patients.

Is there some combination of measures from other countries that the U.S. can utilize in reforming our health care delivery system? Although the overall systems vary, the common factor for all other countries is government-mandated health insurance. Even those countries that have a component of "private" health care continue to mandate that every citizen have government-approved health insurance.

While universal health insurance coverage is a worthy goal, the critical point is utilizing the best mechanism to allow the greatest number of Americans access to health care. Simply having health insurance in no way guarantees timely access to health care. The American experience with the Veterans Administration hospital system, a comprehensive government-controlled, single-payer health care program, reveals unacceptable wait times and huge inefficiencies.

The United States distinguishes itself from other countries by a broader use of free markets. Just like all other economic activities, the free market offers the best solution to provide the greatest access to health care and to control costs.

Instead of looking to other countries, health care reform in the U.S. should allow Americans to freely make their own health care decisions and use their own health care dollars. This would give Americans the best chance to utilize their right to access health care. Eliminating third-party payers, greater use of health savings accounts, price transparency, and health insurance reform would put patients, rather than the government, in charge of their own health care.

## Personal Responsibility in Health Care; Is it Right to Force the Rest of Us to Pay for Other People's Bad Lifestyle Choices?
*December 9, 2019*

Jason rides a high-performance motorcycle and doesn't wear a helmet or protective gear. Jessica smokes two packs of cigarettes every day and refuses to quit. Jeremy tends to overeat and is 100 pounds over his recommended weight. From a medical standpoint, these are all high-risk lifestyles. To what extent is society responsible for paying for the health care of these individuals, and what is the role of personal responsibility?

Common sense says people understand their lifestyle choices and would have health insurance that covers their choices. It also seems logical that insurance companies that take on risk would charge customers more for policies that cover the life choices that frequently lead to illness and injury.

Unfortunately, that's not the way that health insurance and health care policy have evolved in the United States.

Auto insurance is underwritten, and people demonstrating bad driving habits pay more for their policies. Homeowners with good maintenance, smoke alarms, and security systems pay less for insurance. So why is health insurance treated differently?

It all goes back to how health insurance developed in the U.S. Since 1943, employers have gotten a tax break when providing health benefits to employees in group-insurance settings. There are some modifiers, but essentially employees are lumped together in risk pools regardless of health risks of individual group members. Half of all Americans receive their health insurance from their employer through this type of group-focused arrangement.

Medicare and Medicaid began in 1965, and the Obamacare benefits started in 2014. Forty percent of Americans receive their health insurance through these government programs. There is no significant health underwriting in these taxpayer-funded plans, and, consequently, high-risk lifestyles are not a concern for people in these programs.

The remaining ten percent of Americans are either uninsured or are in the private individual health insurance market, where again, no meaningful risk underwriting takes place.

The question is whether people would alter their high-risk behavior if they were completely responsible for their own health care costs.

Advocates on the political left claim that health care is a "right." How does personal responsibility figure into this belief? Should the rest of us, through taxation, fund health care for those people who choose to engage in high-risk behavior?

Obamacare has proved that the government cannot force people to buy health insurance. Even though the law imposed an individual mandate (that has essentially been repealed), only 40 percent of the 50 million who were uninsured when the Affordable Care Act became law elected to purchase insurance or enroll in Medicaid.

If the government is paying for all medical care, which it does in Medicaid and in a single-payer system, could the bureaucrats outlaw high-risk behavior? Could cigarettes be banned? Could people be forced to be height-weight proportional? Could patients be compelled to be compliant in taking their medications and following their doctors' orders?

Rightfully, these harsh government mandates would be unacceptable to Americans. On the other hand, the financial impact of any high-risk activity should not be shifted onto taxpayers, most of whom lead responsible lives.

The logical solution is to remove the government from our health care delivery system and allow patients, as consumers, to control their own health care dollars and be responsible for their own lifestyle decisions. Meaningful reform would require a change in the federal tax code so individuals could take the same tax break that employers have had for 70 years. It would require provider price transparency, and it would require health insurance reform and the restructuring of the existing government health programs.

When government is in charge of our health care and taxpayers are forced to pay for it, the idea of personal responsibility becomes meaningless. This seems nonsensical, but is tragically a reality.

—